The World of the Wolf

LIVING WORLD BOOKS

John K. Terres, Editor

The World of the
WOLF

By Russell J. Rutter
and
Douglas H. Pimlott

Profusely Illustrated
with Photographs

J. B. LIPPINCOTT COMPANY
Philadelphia & New York
1968

To Wolves

May men learn to appreciate their right to roam
free in the wild places of the world.

Contents

Authors' Introduction

IN THE PREPARATION of this book the authors have had two main objectives in mind: first, to give a reasonably complete outline of all that we know about wolves, either from our personal experience or from the works of others; second, to encourage a more favorable attitude toward an animal which we believe has been misrepresented and persecuted beyond reason for thousands of years.

Because the book was put together by two authors, we think that our readers should know how this was done, particularly as the personal pronouns "I" and "we" are scattered throughout the text.

In setting up our plan for the book, we decided that Pimlott would be responsible for all photographs, and for all the writing except that part which comes under the headings "Spring and Summer," "Fall and Winter," and "The Voice of the Wolf," which would be Rutter's responsibility. When "I" is used it indicates some personal experience of the writer of that particular section; "we" refers to shared experiences or to generally accepted knowledge. Since we felt free to make suggestions and to criticize each other's efforts, it can be considered that we share the majority of the viewpoints expressed.

Until about ten years ago only a few people had learned to write or speak about wolves objectively. Up to that time the only "studies" of wolves, with two or three notable exceptions, had been concerned with methods for killing them, and the natural history of wolves was largely a concoction of myths, legends, exaggerated yarns, and deliberate lies that had been handed down from generation to generation. So deep-

11

rooted was the prejudice inherited from our ancestors that anybody was prepared to believe anything about wolves—as long as it was bad. It is difficult to offer an apology for the otherwise competent and conscientious scientists and writers who have continued to quote without comment from these unsubstantiated tales, many of which are so fantastic that present-day readers, even without any knowledge of wolves, would find them difficult to believe. We can only suppose that even conscientious scientists are not wholly immune to the virus of prejudice against the wolf that has plagued mankind for so long.

It might be said that the wolf was one of the last natural resources to be included in the great modern movement toward conservation. Theodore Roosevelt is often referred to as the "father" of that movement, but his contribution to our knowledge of wolves is summed up in his description of a wolf as "the beast of waste and desolation." We believe that the future of this noble animal will depend a good deal on whether its image in the public mind fits Roosevelt's description or whether it can at last be seen for what it is—an exceptionally interesting part of our wildlife heritage and an outstanding representative of that wilderness which we are belatedly trying to preserve.

We do not make any claim to know "all about wolves" and have tried to make this clear in the text. Most of the references are from the work of people still living, many of them still working on wolves. There are many details in the life history of wolves about which little or nothing is known, but we believe the over-all picture is complete enough to justify this account.

We have tried to show what kind of animal a wolf really is, and we are particularly glad that our information on this important point is almost entirely from personal experience. Both of us have spent years in close association with wolves, both wild and tame, mostly in Algonquin Provincial Park, Ontario, Canada, an area of 3000 square miles, itself surrounded by wolf country. The Park maintains what is probably close to a maximum wolf population and has done so for many years.

Large feet that spread on impact are the wolf's snowshoes.

Footprints of the rear (small) and front feet of a wolf. The lens cap is 2 inches in diameter.

There is nothing artificial about this population, and the wolves are free to cross the Park boundaries in either direction at any time. In the past they have been subject to trapping, snaring, shooting, and poison, but at present they are given the same complete protection as all other animals within the Park boundaries. Any idea that we have attempted to whitewash the wolf's record as a killer of big game will be dispelled by the accounts of its food and hunting.

A naturalist cannot spend much time in Algonquin Park without knowing that wolves are a vital part of the environment. In the soft earth of bush roads and beaches he sees the big, doglike tracks; he finds scats full of deer hair along the trails; as he tends his campfire he hears far away the clamor of a pack's evening howl; in winter he sees the remains of deer that have been killed and eaten on the ice of frozen lakes. He may never see wolves, but he senses their presence everywhere, and soon learns that the better-known animals, the deer, the moose, and the beaver, are only secondary citizens, each paying tribute to the real King of the Forest.

Although we have never restricted our wolf studies to conventional working hours, a large part of our knowledge of the wolf has been acquired in the course of our work with the Ontario Department of Lands and Forests. Without access to the records of their Wolf Research Program, with which one of the authors was closely connected for several years, the writing of this book, in its present form, would have been impossible. The majority of the photographs of wolves were taken during the period of this research. A few of them are the property of the Department of Lands and Forests.

We wish also to express our appreciation for the assistance provided by John Shannon, Paul Joslin and John Theberge, all of whom have been associated with the Wolf Research Program and have carried out original work on wolves in Algonquin Park. The diagrams of wolf chases and kills were executed by Paul Geraghty of the Royal Ontario Museum, Toronto, and we are grateful to him for his co-operation in

Authors' Introduction

this project. George Wilson of St. Louis, Missouri, has made several photographs available to us and has placed no restrictions on our use of his extensive notes on the behavior of his captive wolves. To him, and to all others who have contributed in any way to our work on this book, we express our sincere thanks.

R. J. R.
D. H. P.

Algonquin Park, Ontario
March, 1967

15

The Wolf as a Symbol
of Evil

THE BELIEF THAT WOLVES are dangerous to man is deeply ingrained in our consciousness. In spite of the technological advancement of the age it seems that the fear and folklore of centuries still dominates our thinking when questions of men and wolves are concerned.

Over the years when we have given talks about wolves we have invariably been asked some version of the question, "Will they attack man?" What is the truth? What is the answer to this question that has plagued the relationship of men and wolves throughout eons of time?

Ontario, where we live and work with wolves, is perhaps as good a spot as any from which to draw some examples that will shed some light on the part of the question that applies to the present day. In this area of the world, we believe, wolves are as numerous as they have ever been. In fact, it is probable that they are much more numerous than they were when the first fur traders began to map the interior trade routes. The reason for this, which we discuss in more detail elsewhere, is that primitive forests were dense and, as a result, did not support large populations of the big-game animals that are the primary food of wolves.

We believe, for example, that Algonquin Park has one of the highest wolf populations in North America, perhaps even in the world. Each year thousands of children from the ages of seven to seventeen range widely through it on canoe trips, camping on the shores of isolated lakes and rivers. There have been no records of any of them having been attacked or even threatened by a wild wolf.

Since we began to study wolves in Algonquin Park in 1958, we have at times worked in very close contact with them. In 1961, for example, a young college student, Paul Joslin, maintained contact with a family of wolves—we called them the Source Lake Pack—for several months. When they traveled from one site to another he packed up his tent and moved to their new rendezvous as soon as he located them. At one of these locations he was camped so close to the wolves that he could clearly hear the low vocal sounds of the pack as they went about their day-to-day family affairs. It seems inconceivable that animals with

A young female.

Coniferous wolf country is a land of many lakes and rivers.

such acute senses as wolves have were not aware of his presence, yet he was never molested in any way, and had no sense of personal danger. An interesting aspect of our work has been that we have done a considerable amount of it at night, a time when both wolves' and man's imaginations are most active. We have found that our imaginations can be our worst enemy, particularly when we are working alone at night and wolves are nearby. Gradually you learn to control fear, and then the work becomes more satisfying and interesting.

Dr. Doug Clarke, who is now Chief of the Fish and Wildlife Branch of the Ontario Department of Lands and Forests, told of one of his experiences with wolves in a way that brings out clearly how our attitudes can condition our interpretation of experiences with wild animals. The following quotation is from one of Dr. Clarke's unpublished papers, "The Beast of Gévaudan," which I shall refer to in more detail later.

Once, in the Yukon, where all the wolves are the size of the Beast of Gévaudan, I was returning to camp by night over a snowy trail when I came suddenly on the steaming-beds of several of them. I continued, not even curious, because I had behind me 16 years of familiarity with wolves. Before long, however, I realized that even if I was not curious the wolves were. Two fresh tracks cut the trail in front. Although I could not make them out, they were sometimes in front, sometimes behind, sometimes on one side, sometimes on the other. After about three miles they wearied of the game and I knew that they were no longer with me. I was hungry, if they were not, and in a hurry, and I just kept on going without giving them much thought. When a ruffed grouse burst out of the snow at my feet I may have jumped an extra inch or two, but I can truthfully say I was not what some writers have called "edgey."

What kind of story would Dr. Clarke have told about this experience with wolves if he had feared them, or if he had been certain that they were intent on making a meal of him?

There were two other incidents in Paul Joslin's Algonquin Park adventure that give some insight into a part of a wolf's behavior and little has been written about it. That is their ability to command a situation by threatening to attack when their rights are being challenged. The second year that Paul Joslin studied wolves he located and tried hard to keep in contact with a group that we called the Fool's Lake Pack. It was a large pack and much more difficult to stay in touch with than the smaller Source Lake Pack had been the previous year. One night, a very dark one, he had located them by getting them to reply to his imitations of their howls. He was well up on a hill and they in the bottom of a V-shaped valley below. He wanted to be certain of their location, so immediately began to work his way down the hillside toward them.

19

Part way down he suddenly became aware that there was an animal very close to him, for he could hear its footsteps rustling in the leaves and grass on the ground. As he stopped, the wolf began a harsh, challenging series of barks. During the next five or ten minutes the wolf repeated the sequence twenty-seven times before he withdrew. There were nine animals in the pack and no single unarmed man could ever have fended them off if they were ever to make a serious attack. The situation would seem to have had many of the elements that should have provoked an attack: a man—an enemy—under cover of darkness, sneakily approaching a family of wolves with pups that were still too young to move with the pack in their hunting forays. Yet all the wolf did was to approach and threaten by barking harshly twenty-seven times.

There was a similar incident when my wife Dorothy, my daughter Janice, and I were observing a family of wolves in the Annie Bay Burn in the Park. It was late afternoon, but still daylight, when the female became aware that we were watching them from the open face of a small hill. She became alert but showed no evidence of alarm. For several minutes the observing was mutual—wolf watching people, people watching wolf. Finally, she seemed satisfied and began to move slowly around the resting site and, a few minutes later, along a game trail that followed the edge of the bog which separated us. After moving slowly away along the trail for about two hundred yards, she left it and began to pick her way across to our side of the bog. She was still gradually moving farther away from us. In a minute or two she reached our side and disappeared into a strip of forest that had escaped the fire. We then turned our attention back to the resting site to watch for the remainder of the wolf family.

In a few minutes the male wolf appeared, and our attention focused on him; at the same instant we were startled by a harsh challenging bark from the edge of the trees only 50 feet behind us. The doglike barking challenge was repeated over and over again. We forgot all about the rest of the wolf family in our momentary consternation. The barking wolf, which was probably the female we had seen earlier, remained just out of our sight in the trees—but so very close. Eventually my wits returned, and I switched on a tape recorder that I had brought along and began to record this strange vocal performance. Only then did we remember to look for the male wolf, but in vain; he had disappeared.

The barking challenge continued, but by then we had regained our aplomb and were busy recording and, occasionally, howling back to see what her response would be. After a time she began to move slowly away, continuing to bark the same deliberate sequence all the while. As the distance increased, the barking gradually changed to howling, but still in the unusual sequence of the earlier barking. When she reached the top of the hill, a quarter of a mile or so away from us, the barking ceased and we became aware of the silence of the deepening

The friendly gaze of a wolf. (George Wilson)

twilight that was closing down around us. In this silence we collected our gear and made our way back to camp, still experiencing tingles up and down our spines as we relived our strangest encounter with a wolf.

This again was a presumably explosive situation, the invasion of an area where there were pups, but again all the wolf did was to bark at us. There were many other instances when we were as near to wolves but did not have our presence recognized even by barking.

Dr. Adolph Murie has worked close to wolves for years and has many interesting stories to relate. In 1940, when he was doing the field research on which his book, *The Wolves of Mount McKinley,* is based, he crawled into a den in which there were six wolf pups less than a week old. The parents, present at the time, moved off several hundred yards and howled and barked at him but made no effort to come close, although he took one of the pups with him.

For years the late J. W. Curran, editor of the *Sault Daily Star* (Sault Ste. Marie, Ontario), maintained a standing offer of $100 for anyone who could prove that he had been attacked by a wolf in the Algoma District of Ontario. In his book *Wolves Don't Bite,* Mr. Curran stated that "80 or 90 claims have been made for the money . . . but few of the claimants could be induced to answer the questions submitted to them by the Star." Mr. Curran wrote:

All of the claims from Algoma district were more or less investigated. It was found that some of these were made to cover up the breeding of wolves or the use of poison. Many were based on the desire to figure as a hero. Some were made by people who really believed they had been the objects of attack. In none of the claims investigated was there a trace of wolf hostility.

Every year or two, gruesome, vivid stories of wolf attacks on humans are reported by the various news media. They are often carried around the continent by the wire services. The Department of Lands and

The Wolf as a Symbol of Evil

Forests now assigns a conservation officer or biologist to investigate each incident that is reported. None have stood up to the investigation. Invariably the accounts are found to be greatly distorted.

Recently, in the fall of 1963, a farmer who lived in an isolated area of the province was attacked by a wolf as he stepped out of the building. The bite was in the throat area and could have been fatal. I discussed the incident with the biologist who investigated it. The farmer's story was quite different from the one that appeared in the press. The wolf had come into the farmyard and got into a fight with a dog. The farmer was bitten when he was trying to break up the fight. Such wounds are often received by dog owners when only pets are involved.

An interesting aspect of the story is that the farmer insisted that he had described the incident as it happened. It was apparently developed a "little" to make it into a more readable story. Such distortion is an important element of virtually every wolf-human incident.

The one record of a wolf attack on a human that seems to bear consideration occurred in Ontario in 1942 and was reported in *The Journal of Mammalogy* in 1947 by Dr. Randolph Peterson of the Royal Ontario Museum. The account quotes sworn statements made by a railway section foreman, Mike Dusiak, who was attacked by a wolf, the train crew that killed the wolf, and the conservation officer who investigated the incident.

Dusiak was driving his speeder along a railroad main line, west of Chapleau, Ontario. He was expecting to meet a train and was driving slowly so that he would have time to remove his speeder from the rails. Dusiak wrote of the attack and of subsequent events in these words:

Suddenly something hit me and grabbed me by the left arm. It came so fast and was such a blow that it pulled me and the speeder from off the track by the impact on to the south side of the rails. It happened so fast and as it was still very dark, I thought an engine had hit me first. After getting up from out of the snow very quickly, I saw the wolf which was about fifty feet away from me and it was coming towards me. I grabbed the two axes, one in each hand and hit the wolf as he jumped at me right in the belly and in doing so lost one axe. Then the wolf started to circle me and got so close to me at times that I hit him with the head of the axe and it was only the wielding of the axe that kept him from me. All this time he was growling and gnashing his teeth. Then he would stop circling me and jump at me and I would hit him with the head of the axe. This happened five times and he kept edging me closer to the woods which was about 70 feet away. We fought this way for about fifteen minutes and I fought to stay out in the open close to the track. I hit him quite often as he came at me very fast and quick and I was trying to hit him a solid blow in the head for I knew if once he got me down it would be my finish. Then in the course of the fight he got me over onto the north side of the track and we fought there for about another ten minutes. Then a west bound freight train came along travelling about thirty miles an hour and stopped about half a train length west of us and backed up to where we were fighting. The engineer, fireman and brakeman came off the engine armed with picks and other tools, and killed the wolf.

The conservation officer who investigated the incident and examined the wolf stated that the wolf was not an old animal and was in good condition. It was not, however, tested for rabies, for this was not routine then as it is now. The behavior of the wolf suggests that it was rabid. Anyone who has worked closely with wolves and knows how wary and quick-moving they are realizes that a normal wolf is most unlikely to stand its ground while being attacked by men with shovels, as happened in this instance.

Documented accounts of evidence that wolves attack or threaten men in North America are extremely rare. It would not, I feel certain, be an exaggeration to state that of every 1,000 lurid accounts at least 999 have been exaggerated or are figments of the imagination.

What about the wolves of Europe and Asia—the packs chasing the troika and the other accounts that suggest a much more aggressive behavior of wolves toward men in that part of the world? Could it be that a different situation exists or at least did exist there?

In a paper called "The Grey Wolf," Colin Matheson refers to many of the published accounts of attacks on people in Europe; it certainly seems beyond question that attacks, some of which were fatal, did occur. In the "Beast of Gévaudan," Dr. Clarke reviewed the question in considerable detail. He pointed out that in the Scandinavian countries the story is similar to that in North America—there is little evidence of humans being attacked by wolves. In Central and Southern Europe, where people were more numerous and where wolf-habitable country was intimately associated with rough grazing land and fields, the situation seems to have been different. There, attacks on humans were more

With this dense coat, a wolf can sleep on the snow at 50 degrees below zero.

common, and those attacked were frequently killed instantly or died shortly afterwards. After studying the description and results of actual attacks, Dr. Clarke concluded, "Down the long list of recorded attacks by wolves it becomes clear that the Russian baron in his troika is folklore, but the rabid wolf is grim fact. The pattern is universal. The famous wolves of medieval song and story were all rabid."

If rabies is the explanation, why has there not been a similar history in North America? Part of the answer may be the lower density of humans in parts of the country where wolves are common. It may also be true that rabies epidemics have, for some unknown reason, been relatively rare among wolves in North America. In Ontario, for example, during the past decade, hundreds of wild animals have died of rabies. In many areas the fox population has been virtually eradicated. During the same period less than a dozen cases of rabies have been confirmed in wolves. In addition there have been no decreases in wolf numbers large enough to indicate an epizootic disease which is fatal to the animals that contract it.

Dr. Clarke's investigation made clear to him that the pattern in one of the "beast" stories was different. The history of the Beast of Gévaudan was published by Abbé François Fabre in 1901. It was based on parish records and other official documents. The incidents occurred in the regions of Gévaudan and Vivarais in France between 1764 and 1767, and apparently involved two animals. During the period, well over a hundred people were attacked, and sixty-four were killed. Almost all the attacks were on children. One animal was killed in September, 1765, and the second in June, 1767. Both were very large; one weighed 130 pounds, the other 109. The weights of the two animals, and a skull measurement of the larger one, indicate that they would compare with the largest that now exist in the world. They were much larger than the average wolves of Europe. The description of color and skull characteristics also suggested to Dr. Clarke that they were not normal wolves. He concluded that there was a strong probability that they were first-generation dog-wolf hybrids and not pure wolves at all.

To sum up, there is just no creditable evidence that wolves in North America have ever posed a real threat to man. The same thing applies to "normal" wolves in Europe.

Whatever the reason, and I consider this an intriguing question, it is apparent that wolves do not consider men as prey. There are at least three reasons why this may be true. Hunting by wolves, as will be brought out later, is not instinctive but probably is a process learned by experience with the pack. It takes a lot of time and a lot of opportunities for hunting patterns to develop. Man, as prey, seldom offers either of these in an adequate way. A second reason may very well be that wolves have a tremendous ability to read signs. They instinctively recognize aggression, fear, and other qualities of mind which are evidenced in subtle ways by our expressions and actions. Many common behavior patterns of man undoubtedly denote aggression or hunting behavior to wolves. In hunting we stalk deliberately, quietly, as many predators do; in winter we move through the woods and across lakes and streams deliberately, as a wolf does in traveling over his range, hunting for prey. These behavioral patterns probably indicate clearly to wolves that we are superior predators, not prey.

Finally, there may well be subliminal characteristics of the human mind which also influence wolf behavior. Over the past six years I have developed a very close bond with a mongrel dog and, for a couple of years of this time, with a wolf. My actions have so often been anticipated by these animals, in ways that I have not understood, that I cannot rule out the possibility that they enjoy mental processes beyond my comprehension.

In terms of behavior, there are many things that man has in common with wolves. For example, only man and wolves have developed co-operative, purposeful, methods of hunting in groups; in both wolves and men the young are raised by both males and females; both species also maintain a close relationship with their young throughout the

27

juvenile period. It may be that such similarities go deeper than behavior pattern, even influencing wolves' relationship with the human organism, which, from a biological point of view, should be suitable prey for a large predator.

In spite of my love for wolves and my belief that studying wolves is one of the lowest-risk professions in the world, I usually find myself unable to answer the question, "Will wolves attack humans?" with a flat negative. It is always possible that an animal may be rabid. In addition, I think of wolves as being efficient, effective predators who for centuries successfully occupied a considerable portion of the land of the Northern Hemisphere. Their success must in part be the result of their capacity to adapt rapidly to changing factors in their environment. Adaptation and innovation are closely related, and innovation in food habits, in hunting, might on some occasions result in wolves' killing a human.

When the question is asked of me when I am in one of my favorite haunts, Algonquin Park, I often reply, "The possibility of you, or your child, being injured by a wolf while you are in Algonquin Park is no more than one hundred-thousandth of your chance of being seriously injured in some normal type of accident in getting here."

If wilderness is worth experiencing, if wolf-howling is worth hearing, then surely such a small risk is worth taking; we cannot have the temerity to accept the high risk of being killed in getting from our homes to wilderness and then refuse to accept the minimal risk of experiencing that wilderness.

War on Wolves

THE WAR THAT MAN has waged on wolves goes much deeper than the fear he has had for his life or for the life of his children. It is undoubtedly more closely linked to the loss of domestic animals than to the alleged, or very rare, attacks on people.

In recent history this war has also been closely linked with the competition for big-game animals, which man, through the ages, has required for food and now kills primarily for sport and, to put it clearly in context, for recreation.

Primitive people who are primarily hunters do not fear wolves and take a dispassionate view when they kill other animals. In his book *Nunamiut*, Helge Ingstad, a Norwegian anthropologist, tells of the lives of the Caribou Eskimos of interior Alaska with whom he spent a year. He found that the Eskimo hunters prefer to travel alone and do so without fear of wolves. The pelts are of great importance to them, and when they have an adequate supply of caribou meat they spend much time hunting wolves. There is no reason to believe that primitive hunters of an earlier period behaved in any other way, for the wolf probably had many positive attributes. The pelt provided material for clothing, its body and the remains of the animals it killed, food.

The formal declaration of war was undoubtedly made by man the herder who greatly prized his domestic animals and was very jealous of them. The strength of the feeling of primitive herders against wolves is evidenced by the Lapps of Northern Europe. Turi, in his book on Lapland, tells of the invective used by the herders as they killed the

A handsome one-year-old male.

wolves that they captured. In Sweden the Lapps still retain the right to kill wolves in national parks.

In the following pages we will explore the factors other than fear that have caused man to wage war on the wolves, and we will give brief glimpses of the war as it has occurred around the world.

Although the wolf cannot be classed as a predator of man, we certainly cannot claim that he has not been at times an effective predator of man's animals. However, imagination, exaggeration, and distortion have resulted in the portrayal of the role of the wolf as being far more serious than it has really been. Unfortunately, accounts in which all of these elements enter have generally been accepted at face value and quoted in semiscientific treatises. As a result they have been given greater credence than they warrant.

In all the history of the war on wolves I do not know of a single economic appraisal in which the predation of livestock has been evaluated in terms of its importance to the industry. The justification for killing wolves has frequently been no more than that they posed a *threat* to livestock and has never been any greater than the fact that they killed an animal or animals.

It can hardly be expected that this would have been otherwise in the early days of the colonization of the continent. Surely, however, now, when virtually every aspect of our lives is considered in terms of percentage points, we have the right to demand objective appraisals of the economic influence of any predator before massive extermination campaigns are undertaken.

In certain parts of Canada the opportunity for this type of objective appraisal has existed in recent years. One such area is the Central Plateau of British Columbia. There, in a vast expanse, grass and forest lands, game and cattle production, are intricately intermixed and interwoven. The situation is not comparable to that of the prairies, where, once the buffalo and antelope were exterminated, only the cattle remained as suitable prey for wolves. In the plateau country, moose and other usual victims of wolves live in and on the edge of the forests. There it is conceivable that by selective control operations—the destruction of animals that were actually preying on livestock—wolves could have been left as part of the fauna of the area. But some livestock killing did occur and so no other questions were asked. The cattlemen, who wield political power far in excess of their relative numbers, demanded, and obtained, total extermination of the wolves—and a policy of extermination of all wolves within a 50-mile radius of cattle country. At the time that the extermination program was most active, moose,

31

Left: All the young trees in this logged area were being killed by moose. Photo taken in Newfoundland, where there are no wolves. Below: Adult moose, one of the wolf's prey animals. (The tree is not growing out of its head!) (Ont. Dept. of Lands & Forests)

one of the wolf's prey animals, were raiding haystacks and dying of starvation because of the overbrowsing of natural foods by an excessively high population of moose.

Over a large part of North America, including Alaska, Canada and some of the north central states, the killing of livestock by wolves has been of very little economic importance. In these areas the case against the wolf has largely been built on the "depredation" of wolves on big-game populations. The facts that big-game animals had learned over the centuries to live with their predators and that the numbers of wolves must be closely linked with the food available to them were merely vague subtleties that no one considered.

Some of the most prejudiced wolf haters of a half century ago were men who are now often considered to have been the conservationists of

Competing for the smell of a fresh deer track.

that era. For example, Hornaday, who wrote much about the preservation of wildlife, constantly referred to wolves as "vermin."

This hatred must have resulted from the belief that predation by wolves was likely to result in the extermination of some species. It was a time when the loss of a number of species was in many thoughts, so it was understandable that a master predator would be greatly feared.

Within twenty-five years the viewpoint of most scientists had completely changed. Aldo Leopold's book *Game Management* and, shortly after, Paul Errington's studies on predation made a strong impact and resulted in a great deal of fresh thinking. There was, however, no comparable change in the mind of the hunter. Universally, from Mt. McKinley in Alaska to the hunting camps of Ontario and the Upper Peninsula of Michigan, hunters were calling for the extermination of wolves. The tremendous increase in the herds of white-tailed deer, on which wolves feed, that resulted from the regrowth of the forest was not considered by those who hunted deer. The remains of a single deer carcass killed by wolves was enough to start an emotional storm that reached politicians for miles around.

Shortly after I began to study wolves in 1958, I met and learned to like a man who was an extreme hater of wolves and an articulate writer about wolves and deer. Mike Bates, a station agent, hunter, and tourist outfitter, lived in a small settlement on the very northern edge of the range of the white-tailed deer. He had lived through the days when, following logging and a period of moderate winters, deer had become very numerous. As the forests of the area became less favorable for deer and the area was hit by a series of severe winters, the deer population declined. Wolves certainly did prey on them and may indeed have been a factor in their decline. To Mike, however, they were the *only* factor in the deer decline, and anyone who dared to suggest otherwise was soundly berated.

In his writing, he always stressed the malicious nature of wolves and the way in which they tortured their prey. His last article, "Always Cry

Bighorn sheep, prey of wolves in mountain country. (V. Geist)

Beaver may be an important source of food of wolves in the summer. (Ont. Dept. of Lands & Forests)

Wolf," contains this paragraph, "The belly of the mutilated doe was now ripped open, and the two embryos torn out and eaten before the dying mother's eyes. As is common in wolf kills, they finished their feast off the warm body of their still living victim." A variation of the same theme had occurred in everything that he had ever written.

Wolves do sometimes virtually eat their prey alive, not out of malice or to torture but because they are hungry and need to satiate their hunger. They do commonly tear open the stomach of the individuals that they kill; it is natural that they should, for this is the point at which it is easiest to get through the skin so they can begin to feed.

"A predator is any creature that has beaten you to another creature you wanted for yourself." W. O. Nagel wrote in his article, "Predators Are Like People." He stressed that predation is natural and a necessary way of life. The logic of his premise is sound—but the result of predation on a deer, "an animal that doesn't hurt anything," is usually a grisly, gory spectacle, so it is bound to take time to argue the case on logical grounds. It seems likely that emotions and "wanting for ourselves" will continue to spark arguments and political pressures for many years to come, keeping alive the war on wolves in Alaska, Canada, and remote corners of the world.

It is difficult to go back into history and make an objective appraisal of the influence that wolves actually had on the colonization of North America. It is written that in many areas of the eastern United States the rate of colonization was greatly retarded by livestock losses caused by wolves. It seems perfectly logical to believe that this may have been true. The farms of pioneers were small, often isolated islands in a sea of the surrounding forest. The modern steel trap had not yet been developed, and strychnine as a wolf poison did not become a weapon in the war against them until the nineteenth century. Under such circumstances the pioneers were not prepared to cope with wolves that were capable of adapting quickly to new sources of food.

In the East, bounties for killing wolves were paid from as early as

Northern wolf country.

1630. The war on wolves seesawed for almost two hundred years. By the middle of the eighteenth century it was evident that the wolves were losing. The final blow was the extensive destruction of forests east of the Mississippi River. By 1900 the last wolves were killed in many eastern states; it had happened in Massachussetts by 1850, in the Adirondacks of New York, and in Pennsylvania, just before the turn of the century.

West of the Mississippi River it is unlikely that wolves ever exercised much influence on the rate of colonization. By the time the buffalo were exterminated and the Indian "menace" subdued, the exploitation of the new land was progressing too rapidly to be influenced by wolf predation of livestock. In *The Wolf in North American History,* Stanley Young writes,

In the pioneering of the open-range production of cattle, wolf depredations were expected and, to a large degree, tolerated by cattle-men. Losses occasioned by wolves were deemed one of the hazards of the business. Each cattleman at this time took care of his own lands, and all the attendant dangers.

The situation changed rapidly after livestock associations began to be formed in the 1870s. Problems of cattle rustling and wolf predation were of principal concern and gave the new associations focal points around which the interest of members could be rallied. The stockmen could be stoical about the loss of cattle by disease, drought, flood or severe winters, but no longer about predation. It was a controllable factor, and all the tools of war were mustered to fight it.

According to Young, it was an unwritten law that no rangeman would pass an animal carcass without poisoning it . . . in the hope of eventually killing one more wolf. No consideration whatever was given to the destruction of other forms of wild animals that must inevitably have resulted from eating the poisoned animal. Even the ancient European practice of burning thickets and forests along the streams was used to make areas less suitable for wolves.

In prairie country, on the substitute diet of cattle, the adaptable wolf managed to survive for almost fifty years after the hides were stripped from the carcasses of the last of the buffalo. In the grazing country of the mountains, deer, elk, and other big game species were not exterminated. Wolves persisted in these areas well into the present century, for their dependence on livestock was not as great as on the prairies, and the areas were less accessible to trappers.

The final campaign of the battle in the United States began in 1915, when Congress appropriated money for the control of animals injurious to agriculture. Shortly after this the U.S. Biological Survey was made responsible for animal control on all Federal lands. In the next twenty-five years members of the Federal Service, and their co-operators, killed 24,132 gray and red wolves in the United States.

In 1946 Stanley Young predicted that wolves would always inhabit substantial wilderness areas in the United States. He was wrong—gray wolves have now disappeared from all but very small areas in Minnesota and Michigan; red wolves are teetering on the brink of extinction in Louisiana and Texas.

In Canada there were no intensive programs of wolf control by government agencies until the 1950s. Prior to that time all provinces with wolf populations had paid bounties to encourage the destruction of wolves. However, the land was vast, and large areas were relatively inaccessible, so these measures had little influence on the numbers of wolves.

During the past fifteen years the bounty system was discontinued in all provinces and territories, with the exception of Ontario. In 1964 it was reimposed in the Northwest Territories as a result of ill-considered action by the Territories Council.

The control programs operated by the various provinces have invariably been accompanied by strong protestation that there was no intent to exterminate but only to control wolves when there was a valid reason. The program conducted in British Columbia provided clear evidence that in spite of protests this was not always the case. In that province an intensive program was conducted even in the areas where there was no livestock industry and where the big-game animals were scarcely being utilized by hunters. There have been changes in recent years, and now wolves are no longer being poisoned in many wilderness areas. Similarly in other provinces the intensity of control appears to have been reduced during this decade.

The most bizarre campaigns in the war on wolves have occurred in Europe and Asia rather than in America. There, in the Old World, the wolf lived close to man during the thousands of years that civilization developed, and man gradually gained a degree of control of food through the herding of animals and the development of agriculture. For the greater part of this time, weapons were primitive, so the keen senses of the wolf gave it a distinct protective advantage. Men, however, were not easily daunted, and historical documents in the libraries of Europe contain many accounts of the methods that were used to destroy wolves.

Throughout the world innumerable place names have been coined from the word "wolf." Fred Bodsworth points out in his article "An Even Break for the Peaceful Wolf" that "The Louvre of Paris got its name from a glen on the north bank of the Seine long known and feared as the Louvrier, the breeding place of the wolves."

In France an institution for the control of wolves, the Louveterie, has existed for a long time. In his account, "The Grey Wolf," Colin Matheson states,

It is first heard of in the Statutes of Charlemagne, in a passage commending the Nobles to keep two hunters for the special duty of destroying wolves . . . Napoleon I in 1805 ordered the appointment of lieutenants de louveterie, and this office, after varying fortunes and despite the practical disappearance of wolves, has existed in various departments of France down to the present day.

When wolves were particularly troublesome or abundant in France, the militia was often employed to form large-scale battues to drive the wolves from wooded areas so that they could be killed. After the Peace of Ryswick in 1697 the militia of Orleans was reported to have killed two hundred wolves in this way. In spite of the intensive efforts to eliminate them, wolves persisted in France until at least World War I. They were, however, becoming scarce in many areas by the late 1870s.

In Great Britain, possibly because it is an island, the wolf was extirpated earlier than in France. In England it was extinct by the beginning of the sixteenth century. In Ireland they existed up to the end of the seventeenth century. Irish wolfhounds were used to hunt them, although it is not certain how important they were in bringing about their extermination.

In "The Wolf in Scotland," A. W. Harding tells of a facsimile of the Ancient Map of Great Britain which is on the wall of the Sandeman Library at Perth, Scotland. The date on it is 1325-1350 A.D. "In the left-hand corner of the map, representing the north of Scotland, there is a little drawing of a wolf with the words, 'Comitatus de Sotherland Hic habundant lupi.'" Roughly translated it reads, "Territory of Sotherland. Here the wolf is abundant."

Harding traces the record of the wolf, ". . . from the twilight world of legend and fantasy in the writing of Hector Boece, who tells us that Dorvadilla, fourth King of the Scots, 'ordaint that the slayer of one wolf have ane ox to his reward'." A number of statutes were passed in the fifteenth century that required the people to gather together to destroy wolves. Landlords devised an ingenious method for forcing their tenants to comply with the law—they required that estates be cleared of wolves before leases of land could be obtained.

By the early sixteenth century wolves were gone from the south of Scotland and a really determined effort was made to finish the job in the north. Harding wrote of this, "Then the best of all measures was decided upon. If the wolf could not be exterminated by normal hunting methods then their lairs, the forests, must be put to the flame. Thus by the end of the sixteenth century the great forests of Rannoch and Lochaber were slowly reduced to ash." Still the wolves persisted, and it was another 150 years, in 1743, before the last one was killed.

We have little knowledge of the historical aspects of the war on wolves in much of Europe and Asia. It is, however, apparent that it is now being waged very intensively in parts of Eastern Europe and Russia.

In a recent edition of a Russian periodical called *Hunting and Hunting Economy* there is an article by D. Plotnikov entitled "The Dangerous Predator Will Be Exterminated." He recounts that in recent years as many as 8,000 men in 740 teams have been organized to exterminate wolves. It appears that the efforts are successful, for the annual kill of wolves has declined from 42,600 in 1946 to 8,800 in 1963. Poisons are used very widely and very intensively. In the Republic of Jakut almost 100,000 baits were put out between 1961 and 1963, principally from aircraft.

This, other articles, and discussions I had with Russian scientists a few years ago, all suggest that there is little hope for the wolf in the U. S. S. R. The tremendous land area of Russia and Siberia will make it difficult to get the last wolf. It does, however, appear that both the will and organization exist in Russia to accomplish that objective.

Spring and Summer

THE WOLF IS a social animal. The term *lone wolf* is significant because it describes an exception. Normally, a wolf population is divided into *packs,* and a pack is an organization within which every wolf knows its social standing with every other wolf. Each pack has its own territory and operates as a unit in its relations with neighboring packs.

Dr. Niko Tinbergen, an internationally known authority on animal behavior, has described a similar social order among Eskimo dogs in Greenland:

Within each pack the individual dog lived in a kind of armed peace. This was the result of a very strict "pack order": one dog was dominant and could intimidate every other dog with a mere look; the next one avoided this tyrant but lorded it over all the others; and so on down to the miserable "under dog".

We believe this describes the fundamental organization of a wolf pack, but we would add that, among wolves at least, there is always evident a good deal of genuine friendship and even affection. Dr. Adolph Murie, whose work with wolves in Mount McKinley National Park, Alaska, still stands as a model of good field biology, has written, "The strongest impression remaining with me after watching the wolves on numerous occasions was their friendliness."

The greater part of our information on the details of social structure in a wolf pack has been gathered from studies of captive wolves, but the

43

A wolf pack has a strong social organization. The behavior of dominant and subordinate individuals is evident here.

many scattered observations on wild wolves made by many observers over many years lead to the conclusion that captivity does not significantly affect their social behavior.

The word *pack* does not imply any particular number of wolves, except that there are more than one. *Pair,* when applied to any animal, implies a male and female, but two male or two female wolves which stayed

The placing of the muzzle of one wolf on the neck of the other indicates that the wolf on the right is dominant.

together and occupied a definite territory could constitute a pack. Packs of two or three animals are not rare, but the average in undisturbed territory where there is close to a maximum population is in the neighborhood of six.

A *family* consists of a pair and their offspring, and one or more families may occur within a pack. Present evidence suggests that it is unusual

45

This wolf den was formed by a slab of rock that flaked off and slid down the face of the larger rock.

A wolf den—the type that wolves sometimes dig for themselves.

for more than one pair to breed in the same pack in one year. It has been rather generally supposed that a pack is based on a family, but it is a matter for speculation whether the general pack organization or the family exerts the greater influence in keeping the pack together.

The young are born in a den in the spring. In Ontario, dens have been found among the roots of both live and dead standing pines, in hollow logs, under the roots of windfallen trees, in natural caves among rocks, and dug into the sides of sandy hills. The low, rounded ridges of glacially deposited sand, known to geologists as *eskers,* are favored as denning sites, especially on the treeless tundra where natural cavities and good places to dig are uncommon. In such situations in Alaska, Murie found that they often enlarged fox burrows for their own use, and there are records of their utilizing abandoned beaver lodges in the same way.

The entrance to most dens is less than 2 feet in diameter, so an adult wolf must enter in a crouching position, but the passage is usually enlarged within, sometimes enough to allow two animals to pass. Burrows have been reported up to 30 feet in length and as short as 7 feet, but the average is about 12 feet. At the end there is a nursery chamber, but no bedding is used. Sanitary conditions are maintained, however, probably by the adults eating the feces of the young, a rather common habit in the animal world. Often there is only one entrance, but there may be two or more.

In the Brookfield Zoo, at Chicago, according to Jerry Woolpy (a graduate student who visited us in 1965 and was interviewed by Paul Joslin), all members of the pack, which consisted of ten wolves, took part in preparing the den, and all used it at times as a refuge when they were frightened. It is not known if such co-operative effort occurs with wild wolves, but it does seem that the habit of the whole pack's using the den as a hiding place is related to captivity, where normal means of escape are not possible. In a wild state wolves are very much animals of the open, sleeping wherever they happen to be, on the ground or in the snow, and escaping from any supposed danger by running away. They do sometimes take cover from bad weather. Dr. Ian McTaggart Cowan found a pack of five in Banff National Park sheltering under a pile of blown-down pines in winter, and Pimlott reports a pack using natural cavities in a rocky hill in Algonquin Park during a severe winter storm.

Stanley Young, in *The Wolves of North America,* writes: "The female wolf, up until shortly before the birth of the whelps, may clean out or dig several holes besides the one to be first occupied. These dens may be from five to ten miles distant, or again, they may be but a few hundred yards apart." The presence of several dens in the same area, only one of which is in use, has been noted many times, but the explanation for this could be that the same area, if not the same den, might be used for years if the location is favorable. We know of two instances in which the same den was used more than once.

Whether extra dens are prepared deliberately for emergency use is uncertain, but it is true that the young may be moved if the den is disturbed, or sometimes for reasons known only to the wolves. Schön-

Young wolves rest for a moment. Many dens and rendezvous sites are close to water.

berner reports that in the Berlin Zoological Gardens in 1963, a family of six pups were moved four times before they were four weeks old, but we cannot be sure that this would have happened in a wild state.

The reaction of wolves to outside disturbance, by humans or other animals, is variable. At a den in Algonquin Park in 1961, the nursing female was killed by a black bear when the pups were approximately four weeks old. There was no evidence that the bear tried to reach the pups, but they were moved at once to a new location by other members of the pack. In 1963, when this den was again occupied, the four pups were removed, tagged, and returned to the den by research biologists of the Department of Lands and Forests, and again they were moved. During this last operation there was neither sight nor sound of the adults.

In direct contrast to this, Adolph Murie gives a vivid account of crawling into a den and bringing out one of the six small pups, which he carried away in his packsack while the parents barked and howled

Away again.

nearby. To his great surprise when he returned next day, the male wolf was sleeping near the den entrance, and the family did not leave the area until the first week in July, although the den was under constant observation. We can only speculate why there should be such a difference, but it may be nothing more than the variation of temperament among wolves.

When a pup must be moved, before it is able to travel on its own, the adult does not pick it up daintily by the loose skin of the neck. It takes the whole body into its jaws, crosswise, with the head and forelegs protruding on one side and the hindquarters on the other, or else picks it up by the hips, or by one hind leg with the head hanging down, or occasionally by the skin of the belly. I am able to testify that if one does not know that this is standard practice with wolves it is a breathtaking sight to see the tiny body all but disappear well back between the long jaws of an adult wolf, with only a few inches showing at each end—exactly as if it were about to be bitten in two and swallowed.

The average period of gestation in wolves is sixty-three days. According to records from Russia, Europe, and North America, most litters arrive in May, but they may be as early as March or as late as June, with a tendency for earlier dates in the south and later in the north. All births that we have recorded in Algonquin Park, Ontario, where most of our wolf work has been done, have occurred in the first two weeks of May. As many as fourteen pups have been reported in a litter, but five, six, or seven seem to be most common. We have had firsthand experience with three litters of five from various parts of Ontario.

At birth they are short-legged, snub-nosed, rat-tailed little animals, covered by dark brown, woolly fur. They are born with their eyes closed and weigh about one pound. It is understandable that few people have been in a position to say exactly how long it takes a wolf pup's eyes to open, but in two closely observed instances they were noted as fully open in thirteen days.

50

Spring and Summer

About a week after their eyes open they begin to make the first exploratory trips to the den entrance to try out their new gift of sight on a strange new world. And it is a new world that they see in every sense of the word. When their parents mated in February, the earth lay buried under an apparently lifeless blanket of snow; lake and river were scarcely to be told from forest, and the main concern of every living thing was to keep itself alive. Often at night the temperature went far below zero, moisture in the trees exploded like rifle shots throughout the forest, and the lake ice rumbled and groaned like a restless giant turning in his bed. But every day the sun climbed a little higher, the wind blew more often from the south, and now the transition is complete. A landscape that seemed so lifeless and colorless three months ago is rich with the pastel shades of spring. Grass is green on exposed hillsides, insects are on the wing, the air is filled by day with the songs and calls of birds, and at night with the voices of a million frogs come to mate and lay eggs in the abundant water left from the melted snow. Ravens and gray jays have already brought off young from nests built while the snow was still deep; every day more infant animals, from

A two-month-old wolf pup yapping.

mice to moose, add to the expanding demand for more and more food. But if there are many to be fed there are also many to be eaten, and only the luckiest and strongest will survive to insure the balance of a healthy population for another year. Even among the young wolves, with comparatively little to fear from enemies, only the most alert and physically perfect will complete the two years of apprenticeship necessary before they are ready to undertake raising families of their own.

When the month-old pups first venture beyond the mouth of the den, they are still not too steady on their feet, and their eyes have not quite lost the vague, unfocused look of the very young, but under the stimulus of outdoor activity, sight, scent, hearing, and legs develop by the hour. By the time they have lived eight weeks and are changing their food from mother's milk to meat, their legs will be a foot long, the oversize wolf feet will be apparent, and they may weigh as much as 15 pounds. At fourteen weeks they will have coats similar to those of the adults, the slim, tapering puppy tail will have filled out to a good brush, and they will be fair copies of adult wolves, though still with the gangling, clumsy movements with which we are familiar in the pups of domestic dogs. One of the last physical changes, other than general filling out, will be the loss of their milk teeth and their replacement during fall and winter by the teeth that will be their sole means of support for the rest of their lives.

One of the unanswered questions about wolves is "What happens to all the pups that are born each year?" Milton H. Stenlund found that 41 per cent of the wolves in the Superior National Forest, Minnesota, were being removed annually by a predator control program without noticeably reducing the population, and wondered what would happen if the control program was discontinued. This question has been at least partly answered by experiences in other places. In Algonquin Park, Ontario, for many years before 1958 an average of fifty wolves were snared annually. Snaring was stopped in that year to create a more natural situation in which to carry on wolf research. This meant that there were fifty wolves, many of them of breeding age, left in the Park each year that had formerly been removed, and it seemed logical that a general increase in population could be expected. In the next five years, however, there was no significant increase, either in the number of packs or in the number of wolves in each pack. David Mech's study on Isle Royale provided a classic example of this kind of automatic adjustment, which has been called "biological control." When the study began in 1959 there was a pack of sixteen wolves on the island, and when it concluded in 1961 the pack still numbered sixteen, although the wolves were completely protected and there was an abundant food supply.

There is conflicting evidence on the natural mortality of wolf pups. Of two litters in one pack watched by Murie, one of six and one of four, all survived at least until September, but none of them was with the pack the following spring. Among captive wolves, pups have been lost

A wolf pup just beginning the change from puppy to adult hair.

by flooding of dens, by being killed by adults during periods of unnatural disturbance, by a mysterious disease known as listeriosis, and by infestations of ectoparasites (lice). Probably all of these misadventures were in some way related to captive conditions, but they do suggest some of the things that can happen to wolf pups. It is possible that just as fawns are the first deer to succumb to winter starvation due to their inability to compete with larger and stronger deer, many wolf pups, because of immature bodily development, inexperience in hunting, and only partly grown teeth, fail to survive the rigors of winter living. In any event, there is a way in which more or fewer pups survive, depending on the needs of the population.

It is not uncommon for nursing mammals to accept the care of young other than their own, even of other species, and birds that are feeding young will often respond to the begging of strange nestlings. A strong attachment of a mother for her young and great diligence in its care and protection is taken for granted in most animals, but in wolves this instinct extends to a marked degree not only to the father but to all adults of both sexes, and even before they have become sexually mature.

Lois Crisler, in her book *Arctic Wild,* tells of introducing a litter of young pups to a yearling male and female, and how this sexually immature pair at once assumed all responsibility for their care and feeding. This experiment was duplicated by Pimlott in 1961 in Algonquin Park, when he placed five young pups on an island with a pair of yearlings as a part of the wolf research being carried on by the Ontario Department of Lands and Forests. The reaction was exactly the same as in the Crisler case, and resulted among other things in some of the pictures of young and adult wolves in this book. Schönberner, in his study of breeding captive wolves in Germany, tells how a two-year-old female from a previous mating of the same pair assisted in carrying the young from one den to another, brought them food regularly, and often seemed to show more concern than the mother did for their welfare. Woolpy reports that as soon as the pups were weaned in the Brookfield Zoo their care was taken over by one of the unmated females. It is not surprising then that if one, or even both, of a breeding pair should be lost, the pups will be well cared for.

Creatures of small size appear to hold a particular fascination for wolves—quite apart from those times when they think of them as something to eat. Man has been so long conditioned to think of the wolf as a fierce killer—which at times it is—that it comes as a surprise to learn that it has a definite soft side to its nature. We have noticed for years that captive wolves always take a particularly friendly interest in children and small dogs, and wolf pups absorb their attention completely.

I have stood beside the wolf pens at the Research Station in Algonquin Park while a three-weeks-old pup, out of the nursery box for the first time, tottered uncertainly about under the watchful eyes of its proud parents, who were obviously in an ecstatic mood. Occasionally the mother picked it up, by the "whole-mouth" method and with head held high carried it about for all the world to see. The 90-pound father, apparently forbidden such liberty, stopped to nibble it tenderly from time to time. Two adult males in an adjacent pen watched this family scene intently, sometimes breaking into unusually friendly play between themselves, and all the time with expressions that could only be described as beaming.

There was nothing exceptional about this behavior. Describing such a situation soon after the pups were born in Berlin, Schönberner says, "The male and she-wolf 2 (the unmated extra) show very altered behaviour since the birth of the pups. They are no longer interested in the people, but only in the novelty inside the den. Both appear extremely excited." Each of the two pairs of wolves kept by George Wilson, of St. Louis, Missouri, produced a litter of pups in the spring of 1964, but due to a series of mishaps one litter was lost, and as a result the mother of these was temporarily ostracized by the other wolves. Her mate, however, insisted on helping to care for the remaining litter, although he was not allowed any liberties with them until they were a month old. After that he played with them at every opportunity and sometimes enjoyed a turn of "baby-sitting" while their parents slept. Jerry Woolpy says that in the Brookfield Zoo "The actual birth of the pups is a great social event, and all the wolves become highly excited."

Dr. Adolph Murie spent nearly two hundred hours between May 15 and July 7, 1940, watching and recording activities at the wolf den from which he had removed one of the six pups already mentioned. The location was in the mountainous tundra country of Mount McKinley National Park, Alaska, and from a ridge within a half mile of the den he had an unobstructed view, not only of the den but of miles of surrounding territory. We are not aware of any comparable study of the home life of wild wolves, and no account of the wolf's world could be complete without a summary of his observations.

There were five adult wolves—the parents, two extra males, and one extra female. All of these rested during most days near the den, but occasionally some of them would go for a short hunt in daylight or would not return from a night's hunting. If they missed one day they invariably returned the next.

Considerable ceremony often precedes the departure for the hunt. There is a general get-together and much tail-wagging . . . I saw the two blacks and the two gray males assembled on the skyline, wagging their tails and frisking together. There they all howled, and while they howled the gray female galloped up from the den 100 yards and joined them. She was greeted with energetic tail-wagging and general good feeling. Then the vigorous actions came to an end and five muzzles pointed skyward. Their howling floated softly across the tundra. Then abruptly the assemblage broke up. The mother returned to the den to assume her vigil and four wolves trotted eastward into the dusk.

Of the wolves' return in the morning, Murie continues,

Just as a laboring husband comes home to the family each evening

56

after working all day, so do the wolves come home each morning after working all night. The wolf comes home tired, for he has traveled far in his hunting. . . . When he arrives at the den he flops, relaxes completely, and may not even change his position for 3 or 4 hours. . . . The five adults might be sleeping a few hundred yards apart or three or four of them might be within a few yards of each other.

No wolves except the mother entered the den until the pups were about two weeks old, but after that the father and the extra female could go in. These two were as attentive to the pups as their mother was after they began to play outside, and on at least three occasions the extra female stayed all night with them while the mother joined the hunting pack. The two unmated males allowed the pups to climb all over them in their play and sniffed at them curiously, but otherwise took no part in their care except by bringing food to the den. As with all children, the pups often persisted in their play to the point of annoyance, and all adults were forced at times to move to a new spot farther from the den in order to get some sleep.

Food may be carried to the den in the jaws or it may be swallowed and regurgitated. It seems probable that bony parts, such as legs or skulls, are brought by the first method and boneless meat by the second. Schönberner noted that in September "The adults bite hard bones to bits and then leave them to the young," and relates this to the pups' tooth development. Lois Crisler writes that meat disgorged for the pups looked so fresh that "It could have come from a market counter," and records one case in which it had been carried eighteen miles, but "only the last portion to come forth was tinged with brown . . . the rest was still fresh and red." Food brought in either way is sometimes buried in the general vicinity and utilized later by both pups and adults. In burying food the wolf prepares the place by scratching with its forefeet, but always covers it by pushing the earth back into position with its nose, a practice also followed by the red fox.

When an adult returns to the den from a hunt without any visible

57

When the adult wolves return from a foray, the pups bite their mouths and necks. This may be to stimulate the adults to regurgitate food.

food, it is besieged by the pups, which crowd around it, centering their attention on its mouth. This appears to stimulate regurgitation. When pups were first introduced to the Crisler adults the female "threw up," although she was unable to deliver any food, and the male, who had

just been fed, lost his supper to the pups. Meat is regurgitated volun-
tarily, however, when it is to be buried for future use. The instinct seems
to operate automatically at times with no practical purpose, or as
though it had a ritualistic significance, as when a captive female was
seen to eat a can of dog food, only to call the pups to her at once and
regurgitate it. It seems reasonable that such an instinct might develop
in an animal which often must travel many miles to obtain food and
transport as much of it as possible over great distances in the shortest
possible time.

The World of the Wolf

The only reference we have seen to wolves bringing living prey to the den is by the Russian L. P. Sabaneev, cited in Ognev, *Mammals of Eastern Europe and Northern Asia:* "At about this time (1½ months) the older wolves carry young animals to their young, first dead ones, then half-living ones, as the cat brings mice to its kittens."

Sounds uttered by adults to call the pups have been described by Pimlott as "intense whimpering" and are among the many vocal sounds from wolves below the level of howling and barking. They are all difficult to describe. Lois Crisler speaks of some wolf language as "a long, fervent string of mingled crying and wowing . . . like nothing else on earth." Schönberner mentions the male parent "whining rhythmically" when the pups are small, and the pups uttering "soft, high sounds, heard in particular during nursing." Our Research pups would try to howl in response to recorded howls or imitation howls before they were three weeks old, and at three months their howling could sometimes be mistaken for that of adults. Tame wolves whine very much like dogs and for similar reasons.

There is a widespread idea that wolves change their food habits with the seasons, hunting big game in fall and winter but living mostly on mice, rabbits, birds, and other small animals for the rest of the year. This assumption may be encouraged by the fact that summer kills of big game by wolves are seldom found, whereas in fall and winter they are relatively conspicuous. There are also many more men interested in such matters abroad in deer-wolf country during fall and winter, because this is the time when most of man's hunting is done.

According to an extensive study of the wolf's food habits carried out in connection with the Wolf Research Program of the Ontario Depart-

Opposite: In some areas, white-tailed deer fawns provide much food for wolves during the summer. (Top photograph, Ont. Dept. of Lands & Forests)

ment of Lands and Forests, big game forms the bulk of the wolf's food throughout the year in Ontario. In winter the study was accomplished by tracking wolves to their kills, as well as by analysing droppings, or scats, and in summer by scat analysis only. A total of 1435 scats were collected in Algonquin Park from 1959 to 1964, of which 1148 contained deer, 122 moose, 101 beaver, and the balance hare, rodents, and miscellaneous smaller animals. When summer scats were separated from winter, the same proportion—actually slightly higher—contained deer remains. Studies in Wisconsin, Minnesota, Michigan, and Alaska also show that wolves are very dependent on big game for food.

The wolf is a clever opportunist about its food-getting, and relies on the prey that is most readily available in the largest quantity with the least expenditure of energy. It would require a tremendous number of rabbits or mice to support a wolf pack, and even if they were available in sufficient quantity it would mean more work to obtain enough than it would to kill an occasional deer, or moose, or caribou.

An interesting point is that in Algonquin Park 71 per cent of the summer scats contained fawn hair but that in the winter only 15 per cent of the deer killed were fawns. At that season the highest kill was of deer five years old and over. Comparable figures for adult and calf moose were obtained by Mech in Isle Royale National Park. Selectivity in big-game animals killed by wolves will be discussed further under winter hunting.

Wolf pups exhibit the playfulness common to all young animals, and most of their play activity is such as will develop the skills necessary to their survival in later life. Chasing each other, fighting mock battles,

Opposite: Wolf pups at this age play hard for long periods at a time. Below: Wolf pups see something of interest. (E. C. Walsh)

and chewing up anything they can get in their mouths are the basic elements of most of their play. They especially like to take things apart, or to move anything movable. Anyone working with a litter of wolf pups soon learns to guard such things as shoelaces, hat, and gloves, as these are sure to receive special attention.

As they grow older, wolf pups indulge in long games of tag, and also do a great deal of jumping, charging, and ambushing. There is, in fact, a rather definite pattern to their play in relation to age. In the first six months they are full of curiosity and experiments; in the second half of their first year their play becomes very rough, and children who have played with them up to that time are likely to find their rough-and-tumble romping too strenuous. At that stage their idea of a friendly greeting may take the form of a wild charge which can easily knock you off your feet. This football-tackle stage foreshadows the tactics that will be used later to knock down a deer, but it is also one of the many habits shared by wolves and dogs.

When the pups are about two months old the family leaves the den and, with the rest of the pack, moves to an outdoor location, variously called a rest area, loafing spot, or rendezvous, which will be used as headquarters for rest, play, and feeding until the pups are old enough to travel with the pack.

We can only guess why the move is made, but there are several reasons that seem logical. The pups have more than doubled in size, and even if they wanted to use the den it would be overcrowded; the area is in a much "used" condition, fouled by the remains of food and feces; and the activities of rapidly growing pups require more room.

Why a particular site is chosen is again only a guess, but they do have

Opposite page, top: A typical wolf rendezvous site in Algonquin Park. Bottom: Good country for wolves and moose.

certain constant features. In Algonquin Park they have always included a considerable grassy area, such as a dry marsh or an old burn, and Murie describes a similar situation in Alaska. If there is an established food supply along with other suitable features, that might be a deciding factor. An Algonquin Park rendezvous occupied from July to September included the carcass of a large bear, which was completely consumed before the wolves left. Research workers have staked out deer carcasses in the vicinity of a rendezvous and have had some success in attracting both pups and adults into favorable positions for observation—an important consideration in heavily forested country.

We usually find a rendezvous easier to locate than a den. The pups howl very readily at this stage and the goings and comings around their headquarters give much occasion for vocal communication. Up to this age the voices of pups are generally distinguishable from those of adults, and pup and adult voices coming from the same place day after day is likely to mean a rendezvous at that point. Once we learned that wolves would often respond to recorded howls, or even to an imitation howl by the human voice, locating them became comparatively easy.

Finding wolves by howling is one of the most thrilling sports I know, but it has its frustrations. In July, 1965, two of us howled from the highway near Sunday Creek in Algonquin Park at midnight and had an enthusiastic response from a pack that contained pups about a half mile to the southeast. We assumed that we had found a rendezvous, as there had been one near there the year before, but howling on subsequent nights brought no response, and we never did find them again. Considering the date, it seems quite possible that we had intercepted a pack moving from a den to a rendezvous, but where it was is still their secret.

It is never safe to generalize on the activities and responses of wolves, as the following two incidents suggest.

In August, 1960, I spent several hours one afternoon with a litter of four pups installed on an island for research purposes. I had known

A black-phase pup three months old.

Almost every black wolf has a white spot on its chest.

these pups since they were about six weeks old and was accepted as one of the pack, moving when they moved, lying down when they lay down, and so on. At this time they were between three and four months old, and had had no contact with adult wolves since they were taken from the den. They had grown up this far in close association with the Pimlott family, and were completely oriented toward humans for food and friendship.

On this occasion the Pimlotts were away, and I had gone to the island with a photographer to obtain some close-up pictures. After wandering around for an hour or so, the pups and I lay down for a siesta at the north end of the island. The pups were spread over an area about 20 feet square, each in its own little hollow, and I lay beside one of them with my hand on its fur.

Unknown to me, a member of the Department of Lands and Forests research team who had been working to the north of us was at that time walking along a trail that skirted the shore of the lake, and as he passed the island he saluted us with a single howl. The result was galvanic. Every pup leaped straight up as though shot from a spring and at the same instant burst into clamorous howling. Still howling, they ran a hundred feet in the direction of the single howl and there stopped to listen. There was no response, and they gradually settled down to waiting. For it seems obvious in this case that they were waiting; they knew the rest of the pack were away and expected a signal of their impending return.

In the second instance a different set of circumstances brought different results. On an evening in August, 1962, I was with John Theberge on a hill overlooking a "planted" deer carcass, watching three pups playing among the scattered shrubs and fallen logs on a brulée. The play consisted of an endless game of tag, with occasional short rests during which the pups watched us—for they were well aware of our presence.

There were two or three adults moving about independently within a half mile of the pups, and during our watch, which lasted about an hour, these kept up an intermittent howling, but the pups appeared to pay no attention. They were not waiting for anything; they knew where the adults were; the adults were probably just watching the general situation, and their howling may have been to keep contact with each other, or with the pups, or only as an outlet for their nervousness stimulated by our presence.

Interesting results may be obtained sometimes by walking directly into a rendezvous. The pups are more inclined to hide than to run away, which means that their parents will not go far either, and there is a good chance of seeing both.

In the late summer of 1964 a pack with pups was established in a rendezvous behind Eos Lake, about one half mile north of the highway. Several people reported seeing wolves on the highway near this point in late July, and they were first heard howling on August 2. At this time Algonquin Park is crowded with tourists, and on August 27 we had six hundred people out at night to hear the wolves howl. It was an exciting evening, as most of these people had never heard or seen a wolf in their lives and they thought it was a tremendous adventure—which it was.

On September 13 I decided to walk in to the rendezvous to see if I could see any of the wolves. I left the highway at 3:15 and went around the end of Eos Lake and followed the small creek that flows from the lake into a wide valley which was once a beaver pond but is now dry and grown up with grass and sedges. It was a fine, sunny day, the fall colors were very beautiful, and as soon as I was a quarter of a mile from the highway I felt quite alone in the wilderness and was prepared to meet a wolf.

About three hundred yards from the end of the lake I was crossing a grassy opening and trying to identify several trails which seemed to lead down to the creek when a movement ahead caught my eye, and I looked up to see an adult wolf standing on a moss-covered mound of

69

A four-month-old pup on a lookout rock.

rock only a hundred feet away. It was a big, rangy, light-colored animal that reminded me of our tame wolf Dagwood. There were two pups, one on each side, less than one-third the size of the adult and colored dark brown. They were jumping up towards the adult's mouth as though expecting food. None of them seemed to be paying any attention to me, but the old wolf knew I was there, all right, and about fifteen seconds after I had seen them the pups vanished down the other side of the rock, although I saw or heard no kind of warning. The adult stood there for nearly a half minute after the pups left, looking about very casually but never directly at me, then it also disappeared. My interpretation was that the pups had been playing around the rock when the adult became aware of my approach and came to send them

A four-month-old female, in the normal grizzled-gray color phase.

away. It was the movement when it came out on the rock that caught my eye.

I walked ahead to the rock where the wolves had been and looked around, but did not find much except chewed-up sticks and birch bark and old logs pulled apart by the playing pups. There were trails in all directions out into the marsh grass, and three hollows where adult wolves had been lying. There was no sign of food, and the ground was mostly hard and dry and did not leave tracks. I remembered that Adolph Murie did not find any food remains around the den that he had been watching for over a month, although he knew there was some cached in the vicinity.

I went on to where the creek goes down through a small canyon into

71

the valley and sat down to wait for something to turn up. I had been there only a few minutes when another adult wolf, somewhat smaller and darker than the first, appeared on the other side of the creek, loping along in my direction as though heading for the place where the other wolves had been seen. I sat quite still, but at about fifty yards it saw me, stopped and stared intently for several seconds, then bounded away up the slope to the east and out of sight. It appeared to see rather than smell me, but it was downwind and may have got both sensations at the same time. I wandered around a bit more but saw no further signs of life, but the next night, September 14, the wolves answered our howls from the same spot, so they were not much alarmed by my intrusion.

There are many references in literature to young wolves' being "taught" to hunt and kill by adults, and we have been told by old-timers that this is one of the chief activities between the time they leave the den and when they start to run with the pack; in other words, when they are in their rendezvous. There is little real evidence to show that any wild animal deliberately teaches its young anything, except by example. At least for the first four or five months of their lives young wolves are exceedingly timid and show no sign of having been born with any of that ferocity usually associated with a wolf. Lois Crisler found that her captive pups were afraid of caribou, and approached one that had been disabled by a dog with much hesitation. There might be less of this attitude shown by wild pups, since from the beginning they would be conditioned to the pursuit and killing of prey. Wolves must kill to live, and there would seem to be no necessity for teaching the pups. They would learn quickly enough by joining in the normal pack activity. Murie noticed pups hunting mice while they were still at a rendezvous, and it is not impossible that wolves' preference for grassy areas is influenced partly by the hunting possibilities which these provide for the pups.

Young wolves do not show any marked fear of man during their first

72

A wolf pup chasing a frog.

three or four weeks, but if they are not handled daily they become increasingly shy after that, and at two months are quite wild and would probably be difficult to tame. Schönberner says of his European wolves that on their forty-first day they "do not appear to notice me and do not show any reaction to the warning of the adults." But on the fifty-ninth day they show "in contrast to the nearly tame parents a great shyness towards people." The adult wolves kept by George Wilson in St. Louis were all of zoo ancestry and were as tame as family dogs, but their pups, born in 1964 and not regularly handled when small, were unapproachable when they were eight months old. No effort was made to tame the pups born at the Wildlife Research Station in Algonquin Park in 1965, and they showed no fear at three weeks, but at two months I found them terrified at my close approach. They defended

73

A cool spot among the ferns, a typical resting site in the heat of the day.

themselves vigorously by biting when I tried to handle them, although their three-year-old parents were completely tame.

Adult wolves have no enemies except man, and their watchfulness makes it unlikely that the pups could be preyed on by any of the other carnivores. Bears sometimes visit wolf dens, but they are attracted by the meat that has been brought in by the wolves, and it is doubtful that they have any interest in the pups. Once I watched a black bear approaching our kitchen in Algonquin Park to look for food scraps, and the route it was following took it within a few feet of a wire-mesh pen containing a small red fox cub that I was raising. The little fox was very much disturbed, but the bear did not even pause to look at it.

74

A wolf pup having a drink. The black spot on the tail is apparent.

Adolph Murie describes several encounters between grizzlies and wolves in Mount McKinley National Park in Alaska. On one occasion an adult female grizzly and three yearlings visited a den and remained for about an hour, digging up meat that the wolves had cached in the vicinity. During the whole time they fought a lively battle with four adult wolves but were able to hold them off and complete their purpose. On another occasion a single adult male grizzly approached the same den and was intercepted by five wolves when it was about a hundred yards away. When the wolves rushed toward it the bear turned and fled, but was soon surrounded. There was a running fight for about fifteen minutes with no injury on either side, but the bear then retreated and did not return. It was obvious that the wolves were afraid to close with the bear and they were much too quick to allow the bear to catch them, so it was a dangerous game of tag more than a fight. In this same area bears and wolves frequently fed at the same garbage pit. Sometimes they had short skirmishes there, but the size and weight of the bears against the speed and agility of the wolves prevented actual physical contact. Often, however, there was such a near miss as to suggest that a wolf might be killed by a bear. If they did come together the bear would have a decided advantage, with its superior size, weight,

75

protective covering of long hair, and claws and teeth against the wolf's teeth only.

Two instances in Algonquin Park are the only ones we have seen recorded of contact between the black bear and wolves, but it probably occurs as often as with grizzlies. All the signs around the den where the mother wolf was killed indicated an encounter such as Murie describes, but this was one case where the wolf was not quick enough. The dead wolf was about one hundred yards from the den, her ribs crushed as though from a heavy blow or perhaps from the traditional "bear hug." Murie noted that the grizzly did not attempt to strike the wolves, but seemed to be trying to seize them with both front paws. An autopsy of the female killed by the black bear showed five fresh placental scars, identifying her as the mother of the pups.

On another occasion an encounter between a black bear and wolves was witnessed by Wolf Research personnel who were watching an area occupied by a wolf pack. The bear crossed the wolves' territory, harassed by the pack, sometimes chasing and sometimes being chased, but no damage was done on either side.

There is considerable evidence that wolves have a special liking for the flesh of the bear. Besides the one that was eaten at the rendezvous already mentioned, they habitually eat the "nuisance bears" that are shot in Algonquin Park, if they are left in an available situation, and we were told by one experienced wolf trapper that he had found the flesh of the bear to be very effective wolf bait.

The wolves did not leave their Eos Lake rendezvous until after the end of September, but in early October they had moved about two miles south of the highway, and although they remained in this general area through the fall and winter, they were not again tied down to any particular spot. Since early spring their movements had been constantly influenced by the presence of dependent young, but until the next spring they would be held together only by the social organization of the pack.

Fall and Winter

IN MANY WAYS, fall is the most carefree season in the life of the wolf. The responsibility connected with raising pups is over; the breeding season is still months ahead; there is no snow to make hard work of travel; the weather is neither too cold nor too hot, and food is plentiful. The main prey species, the large hoofed animals, are fat after a summer of good feeding, and the smaller ones have also added weight in preparation for hibernation or against the winter's cold. Beavers are not only in prime condition but are spending much time on land, cutting food and building materials and moving them to the water before freeze-up. For a wolf, it must be a good time to be alive.

There is no clear-cut line between the home-based life of den and rendezvous and that of a free-running pack. It is a transition that may take several weeks. During the last week of the Eos Lake rendezvous the wolves were often scattered at night, howling from all directions, suggesting the possibility that the pups were gradually extending their range. After they did move across the highway to the south there were indications that the pups did not at once integrate completely with the pack. Joslin found that at this stage the pack occasionally split into two groups, one containing only adults, the other one or two adults and the pups, but this was always a temporary arrangement.

We had an experience that suggested this situation while tape-recording the Sunday Creek pack on October 6, when we were able to get within a hundred yards of an adult with two or three pups while still a mile away from the main pack. This is one of the many points of

77

Investigating a beaver house.

wolf behavior on which it is extremely difficult to get exact evidence, and we must be satisfied with "intelligent guessing." It seems reasonable to guess that the adult pack members, after their restrictive summer life, may be a little impatient with the pups until their running legs become hardened to long nightly journeys.

Apart from inexperience and somewhat under-developed teeth, the pups are in good shape to face the coming winter. All the wolves now have a new coat of fur which will continue to thicken and lengthen until the snow comes, when they will present their most handsome appearance. Wolves develop a thick undercoat of cold-proof wool in the fall which is pushed off by the incoming new coat during the summer.

Besides the social advantages of co-operative effort in raising a family,

Play—a young male sets up an ambush.

the chief benefit from joining together in packs is increased hunting efficiency. Wolves hunt animals much larger than themselves, but compared with the large members of the cat family, for example, they are poorly equipped to kill big game. They are *cursorial* or running animals, not designed, as the cats are, to stalk and pounce, and it is therefore advantageous for them to hunt in packs.

The average pack contains less than ten animals, and it may be supposed that this is a natural development because it is the most practical size. Two wolves could hunt more efficiently than one, but ten or more would have difficulty in finding a meal for all on prey the size of a deer. The only pack that fed entirely on moose and on which we have precise information contained sixteen wolves; even with such large

79

A male wolf scratches after urinating.

prey they had difficulty finding room for all to feed at the same time.

The social hierarchy that exists in a wolf pack is one of its most interesting aspects, and more will be said of it later as it affects mating activity, with which it is closely connected. One feature that could be mentioned here is the "underdog" or "peripheral" wolf, or wolves, at the lower end of the wolves' social scale. These unfortunate animals, and this has been noted in both wild and captive packs, are almost completely excluded from normal pack activity, and in travel they must trail along behind. It has been observed in Whipsnade Park, in England, where a pack of Canadian wolves has lived for many years, that if a peripheral wolf is removed its place will be taken at once by another member of the pack. This suggests that, in some cases at least, there is some sort of psychological need for these socially unacceptable animals to complete the pack organization. A great deal more study is required before such complicated matters are understood.

When an unattached wolf approaches a pack it may or may not be accepted. Following is a condensed account of one such incident witnessed by Dr. Adolph Murie:

On May 31, 1940, all five adults were at home. Shortly after noon I noticed a sixth wolf, a small gray animal, about 50 yards from the others. All the wolves trotted to the stranger and practically surrounded it, and for a few moments I thought that they would be friendly toward it, for there was just the suggestion of tail-wagging by some of them. But something tipped the scales the other way, for the wolves began to bite at the stranger. It rolled over on its back, begging quarter. The attack continued, however, so it scrambled to its feet and with difficulty emerged from the snapping wolves. Twice it was knocked over as it ran down the slope with the five wolves in hot pursuit. They chased after it about 200 yards and the mantled male crossed the bar after it. Four of the wolves returned to the den, but the mantled male stopped half way up the slope and lay down facing the bar. Presently he walked slowly forward as though stalking a marmot. Then he commenced to gallop toward the stranger which had returned part way up the slope. Back on the bar the stranger slowed up, waiting in a fawning attitude for the mantled male. The latter snapped at the stranger which rolled over on its back, again begging quarter. But it received no quarter so again it had to run away. The male returned up the hill, tail held stiffly out behind, slightly raised. When he neared the den the four wolves ran out to meet him, and there was again much tail-wagging and evidence of friendly feeling.

The unfortunate stranger's hip and base of tail were soaked with blood. It was completely discouraged in its attempt to join the group, for it was not seen again. Such rough treatment of individual wolves, if it is normal, would tend to limit the number of wolves on a given range.

There seems to be a suggestion here that, as in human society, the personal dislike of one influential member might be the deciding factor in excluding outsiders. Peripheral wolves may be on friendly terms with some pack members.

Territorialism is common throughout the animal world, and a "home territory" may be that of a single animal, or of a pair, or of an indefinite number in the case of those that live in groups as wolves do. Most animals defend this territory against other members of their own species or against predators, sometimes only in the breeding season, and sometimes throughout the year. Wolves have no predators and are tolerant of other animals sharing their range, but they generally offer an active defense against strange wolves. This may have a direct effect on population density, as Murie has suggested.

Besides limiting the population and thus conserving the food supply, their habit of segregating themselves into isolated packs might retard the spread of epidemic diseases, from which wolves seem to be relatively free. Although there are authentic records of mange, rabies, and arthritis in wolves, there are no completely documented accounts of any disease reaching epidemic proportions. If we accept records from the unscientific world of a hundred years ago, rabies has sometimes been extremely prevalent among wolves, but recent evidence tells us that they are not now important carriers of the disease in comparison with many other animals. They are known to harbor the adult form of at least six different kinds of tapeworm, but there is no indication that these ever produce any serious effects.

In 1960, biologists of the Wolf Research Program of the Ontario Department of Lands and Forests in Algonquin Park found twenty wolf packs on the study area of 1000 square miles. The average number of wolves in a pack was in the neighborhood of five, or 10 square miles

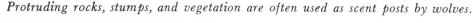

Protruding rocks, stumps, and vegetation are often used as scent posts by wolves.

of territory for each wolf. There is good reason to think that over most of the wolf range of North America the population is spread even thinner than that, but the fact that a similar density was found by David Mech on the undisturbed wolf-moose range of Isle Royale National Park and by Cowan in Jasper Park, British Columbia, during the period of greatest concentration in winter, is significant. It suggests that the density tolerance among wolves does not exceed one wolf to 10 square miles, and that even under the most favorable conditions natural controls would hold the population close to that level.

Although wolves have been said to mark territorial boundaries by scent posts—places where they stop to urinate—there is little real evidence that this is true. A pack would have many scent posts on its territory, and these would mean something to strange wolves, but it is possible that they are nothing more than, as Schenkel suggests, "A peaceful form of contact between neighbors."

While a pack utilizes its whole territory, it may use some parts of it much more than others, and may visit some sections only once or twice a year. This uneven use could be affected by the den location and the distribution of prey species.

Because it is easy to follow the movements of wolves in winter and

Wolves, like dogs, often rub and roll on any particularly interesting scent, in this case that of an otter that came out of the water behind the wolf.

In late winter the snow becomes so heavily crusted that wolves can travel on top of it. There were seven in this pack.

very difficult to do so in summer, our knowledge of their behavior is more detailed for winter than for summer. In winter a wolf cannot move without leaving tracks in the snow, and its color shows up against a white background, so that it is not unusual to be able to trace every movement of an entire pack for hours or even days. In summer, in forested country this is literally impossible, and even on the open tundra

In many areas, frozen water courses become the principal travel routes of wolves in winter.

it is difficult except for local observations. The growing science of telemetry will materially alter this situation, but even electronics can only tell us where a wolf is, not what it is doing.

In spite of this handicap we are able to say with some assurance that wolves travel less in summer than in winter, and that their hunting tactics are somewhat different in the two seasons. The movements of a pack through the year might be diagramed by three concentric rings, the inner circle representing the summer range, the next the expanding range of fall, and the outer the boundaries of the pack territory, or limits of winter range. This, of course, is a general picture, and does not mean that wolves are not sometimes comparatively sedentary even in winter, or that they never reach the limits of their territory in summer.

The World of the Wolf

Wolves are great travelers at any season, and especially in winter, when frozen, snow-covered waterways not only afford level, unobstructed footing but all sorts of short cuts from one place to another which are not available in summer except by swimming.

Wolves are not afraid to swim, but they do not habitually do so in normal circumstances. Four pups used in the Wolf Research Program in 1960 were placed on an island in Algonquin Park because it was thought that the water would act as a fence. Although the pups were less than four months old, they were soon swimming regularly to the mainland and they often played in the shallow water near shore. It seems to be true, however, that various ungulates often escape from wolves by swimming. Many instances are on record of deer, moose, and elk escaping in that way, and Lois Crisler watched a bull caribou take refuge in a small tundra lake while two wolves ran around the shore but would not enter the water.

Much of their travel is correlated with hunting, and it is often hard to draw a line between the two. Field workers in general agree that there is a good deal of apparently aimless wandering. Pimlott and I once followed the tracks of two wolves for the better part of a day, all within an area less than 3 miles square, without seeing anything to suggest purpose in their movements. Another time I trailed a pack of five traveling in daylight between Cache and Ouse Lakes in Algonquin Park, a straight-line distance of less than 4 miles. Although they did no playing around and moved steadily in close formation, their route was very erratic, crossing the highway three times and going straight over steep rock ledges which could easily have been avoided. They traveled at least 6 miles in order to go 4, but paid no attention to several fresh deer trails. As this was not on the territory of any pack, I thought such travel might indicate a pack in strange country, either just looking over the ground, or perhaps uncertain of the best route to follow to get where they wanted to go.

When the snow is deep, wolves sometimes maintain trails so well

86

Resting on a snowy bank after a hard run.

broken at times that a man may walk on them comfortably without snowshoes. These trails serve throughout the winter for both traveling and hunting, as they are often used by game animals after they have been established by the wolves. At the kill near Pewee Lake (described later), one could suppose, judging from the tracks alone, that the

Even moderately deep snow makes traveling hard work for wolves. A deer with its high jumping gait has an advantage over a single wolf at this time.

wolves had spent some time making trails throughout the area before they even attempted to kill a deer.

During that winter there was much evidence that they were having difficulty. More than once I saw where a pack had followed the highway for a mile or more, here and there making a start to leave it, only to turn back after getting bogged down within a few yards. At the time I wrote in my field notes:

The snow is of an unusual granular type with a light crust on the surface, and any long-legged animal breaking through obtains absolutely no footing below. This makes travel particularly difficult for dogs and wolves, and it is quite evident that the wolves avoid making new trails as much as possible. Due to their natural jumping gait the deer have a distinct advantage in this kind of snow. This does not suggest that fewer deer are being killed, but undoubtedly more "wolf hours" are spent for each deer killed.

On February 16 we snowshoed 3 miles north from the Research Station to the Chit Lake Cabin, accompanied by the Pimlott dog, Nutak, who was certainly accustomed to winter travel. In this case, however, he was discouraged long before we reached the cabin, and often lay down in the trail for minutes at a time before he could summon up courage to struggle on. Wolves are a little better equipped than dogs are for deep snow, because of their longer legs, larger feet, and a tendency to bend their hind legs more at the heel, giving their feet greater surface contact with the snow; but they still have trouble.

Mech noted a good deal of what seemed to be aimless travel and found that direction often seemed to be decided by "some unexplained whim," but he also pointed out the necessity to be always on the move if they were to find available prey. In the three years the Isle Royale wolves were under observation they were able to kill only one moose out of every thirteen attempts, and might be required to travel as far as 60 miles before locating a vulnerable animal. Murie comments on the hunting of Dall sheep by wolves in Mount McKinley National Park, "The habit of cruising far in his hunting gives the wolf opportunity to find weak sheep over a large range and to come upon undisturbed sheep, some of which he may find in a vulnerable location." There appears to be a sound base for the old saying, "The wolf is kept fed by its feet."

The extent of travel might be influenced by size of the available range in relation to population. The pack in Burkholder's work in Alaska contained ten wolves and covered an area approximately 50 by 100 miles. Within this 5,000 square miles, their movements averaged 15.5 miles a day, and occasionally reached 45 miles. Once they moved 88 miles in four days. By Algonquin Park standards, a territory of that size could support up to a hundred packs of five animals each, and such extensive travel would be out of the question. Even here, however, we have at least one record of a pack moving 40 miles in twenty-four hours, and Stenlund mentions similar records in Minnesota. Ordinarily, Algonquin Park packs hunt within a territory with a maximum diameter of about ten miles.

Wolves have three gaits—walking, trotting, and galloping. Occasionally they adopt a pacing gait, in which both fore and hind legs on one side are brought forward together, but this is not usual. When they are quartering an area with the hope of flushing game they usually do so at a walk. When moving from place to place they adopt a loose-jointed jog trot which gives them about five miles an hour and can be maintained for a long time. The gallop is generally reserved for pursuing game or playing among themselves.

When snow is deep enough to impede travel, a pack usually moves in single file, stepping in each other's tracks, and this makes it impossible to tell how many animals are involved. Speed of travel, gait, and pack formation are influenced by ground cover, general terrain, and what they happen to be interested in at the time. In one of my notebooks I find the following:

At left, above, a .wolf at a jog trot, its most common traveling gait. At right, a galloping wolf.

Left, a fast gallop.

Wolves can run long distances without rest. They gallop like these two animals only when playing or chasing prey.

Fall and Winter

February 17, 1965. Snow in Algonquin Park is about 15 inches deep and is at present covered by a glassy crust strong enough to support a 150-pound man about 50% of the time. There is a light, irregular snow cover on the crust which helps some, but walking is hazardous, with or without snowshoes. Today I followed the track of one wolf for about a half-mile on the Sproule Lake trail. The wolf had been walking with short steps and never varied its gait. At several places there were marks where its feet had skidded on the slippery surface. The crust would support a wolf or a deer, but a deer might break through if it tried to run. Whether breaking through or slipping on the surface, both animals must be having an awkward time.

Some earlier writers emphasize the supposed habit of wolves of establishing circular hunting routes which are patrolled regularly, but more recent studies have found little confirmation of this. Since they are inclined to spend a good deal of time on the move and do have favored travel routes, some of these are likely to assume a roughly circular form, but the location is probably influenced chiefly by topography, territorial boundaries, and availability of prey.

The wolf is carnivorous, which means that it is a flesh eater. Its teeth are designed for killing prey and for cutting and tearing flesh. Its powerful jaw muscles enable it to crush easily the leg bones of a white-tailed deer. Its metabolism is geared to a steady diet of raw meat. This could be applied just as well to any of the larger breeds of dog, but dogs have become quite omnivorous through close association with man, not perhaps from choice, but from convenience and necessity. The wolf does not have the same choice. Meat is its most available food the year around, and food studies indicate that meat in some form comprises at least 90 per cent of the food of North American gray wolves throughout the year.

Although the red wolf of the southern United States, according to stomach analyses reported by Stanley Young, eats considerable vegetable food, such as mesquite beans, cactus fruits, and persimmons, and G. A.

Novikov reports that wolves in some parts of Russia eat pears, apples, cherries, and ripe watermelons, there is no evidence that North American gray wolves eat a significant amount of vegetable matter. I have seen scats composed almost entirely of grass—too much to be accidental—but analogy with dogs suggests that this probably indicates some disturbance within the animal itself, rather than a choice of food. It is possible that in a southern range, where a greater variety of animal and vegetable food is available all year, the wolf's diet might be more varied, but on the northern ranges to which it is now mostly confined it does not have the opportunity to eat anything but meat, especially in winter.

That wolves share the dog's ability to adapt to other than a meat diet is shown by the captive wolves kept at the Wildlife Research Station in Algonquin Park. There they are fed on a mixture of canned dog food and fox meal, made into a mash by the addition of water, and enriched by cod-liver oil in winter. For between-meal snacks they are supplied with fox pellets, a manufactured product designed, like the meal, for farm-raised foxes. Although they occasionally have a special treat of venison or moose meat from road-killed animals, they are often without this for months at a time, and continue in excellent health and vigor on their "artificial" rations.

All animals that depend on catching other animals for food must be conditioned to irregular meals, and the wolf is used to going without food for variable periods. This is an inherent state in the life of a hunter—"a feast or a famine."

Wolves make up for this by gorging when they get the chance. According to an experiment reported by Young in which captive wolves were placed on a fast and then fed all they would eat, a wolf may eat as much as one-fifth of its own weight at one meal. David Mech estimated consumption of the Isle Royale wolves by taking the approximate weight of moose eaten divided by the number of wolves, and by this method, over three study periods, average consumption of one wolf for one day varied from 9.7 to 13.9 pounds. In several cases he judged single animals to eat 20 pounds in a day.

Several studies have produced figures on frequency of kills. Cowan estimated that a pack of four killed three elk in two weeks; Stenlund's estimate for a pack of three was one white-tailed deer every four days; Mech reports that sixteen killed one moose every three days, and Burkholder's observations suggested that a pack of ten killed either a caribou or a moose every 1.7 days. These figures indicate a rather high rate of food intake, but they can be no more than estimates without knowing the exact degree of utilization of each kill. The Algonquin Park captives, not required to burn up energy in traveling, keep in good condition on individual portions of less than 2 pounds of solid food a day. George Wilson's six wolves, fed on chicken heads and meat scraps, thrived on 75 pounds a week, also less than 2 pounds each a day. In the *Handbook of Travel,* published by Harvard University Press, working dogs in the Arctic are reported to receive 2 to 3 pounds of frozen fish a day, and on this they pull a sleigh, sometimes as much as 50 miles, six days a week.

Just as most animals produce more young than are needed to renew the population, the wolf's instinct to gorge when it has the opportunity

A wolf rarely travels alone in winter.

may cause it to eat more than is necessary. A friend of mine, Abbott Conway, who has shared many of my wolf experiences, owned two Labrador retrievers that we used as sleigh dogs for several years. These dogs weighed between 75 and 80 pounds, very close to the average weight of an adult wolf. On our winter trips they were fed a commercial dog food made to a formula based on experience in feeding dogs used for polar exploration. It was put up in 1-pound blocks, each one intended as a day's ration for a dog working in a nine-dog team pulling 1,100 pounds. This was highly concentrated food, but each of the Labradors would eat five blocks at a meal if given the opportunity.

The following quotation from *Animal Nutrition,* Maynard and Loosli, 1956, might apply in this case:

As the level of food intake increases above a certain value, the ability to digest all of the nutrients tends to decrease . . . High rates of intake reduce the amount of time for digestion and subsequent absorption, and

Wolves are very gregarious. In winter the instinct to travel together is particularly strong.

thus greater amounts of calories are lost in the faeces than at low feeding rates.

The number of large scats often evacuated by wolves in the vicinity of a kill lends strength to this suggestion.

If I seem to overemphasize this question of a wolf's food intake it is because I think the food *requirements* of a wolf are often exaggerated. I have heard estimates of the number of animals killed by wolves based on how much food a wolf *needs* to maintain itself. One of the statements under "Wolf" in the *Encyclopaedia Britannica* is, "The wolf is a prodigious eater." I suspect the wolf eats less and fasts more than is generally supposed.

A long-standing and still common belief concerning wolves is that they show a violent reaction to the sight and smell of blood, but I have seen nothing to support this. I have had sincere people warn me against approaching captive wolves if I had any cuts or scratches, but the worst they have ever done in such cases was to lick the wound, more in a spirit of helpfulness than hunger. More than once, after cutting up a deer for distribution among them, I have had both hands red with deer blood to the wrists, but they still showed no sign of mistaking my hands for venison. Their habit of eating the bloodstained snow around a kill is sometimes used as evidence of their bloodthirsty inclinations, but surely this is no different from one of us cleaning up the juices from a dinner plate. In northern latitudes, snow is often the only source of water in the winter and is eaten by many animals.

Fresh-cut raw meat does provoke a vigorous reaction in captive wolves, but they are probably stimulated at such times by a whole complex of emotions connected with the hunting and killing of prey.

A wolf's first interest on being given a piece of meat is to establish ownership, and it does not attempt to eat until this point is settled. This "guarding" ritual sometimes assumes comic aspects, as when a wolf will lie down with his prize beside a wire screen separating him from other wolves and defy them to "come and get it." If one piece is given to two wolves there is always a short, noisy, but bloodless battle, always won by the dominant animal. If dominance has not been clearly established, the fight, usually a tug-of-war will continue until the meat has been torn in two. On the other hand, if one animal is strongly dominant over the other, and they are given two pieces, it is not unusual for the dominant one to take both pieces and guard one while feeding on the other.

This fighting over food seems to spoil one of the few "good" beliefs about wolves—that they always share the results of a hunt. I suspect that such "selfishness" is aggravated by captivity, where possession of a piece of fresh meat is a rare event. Both Mech and Burkholder observed packs feeding together on moose or caribou without fighting between individuals. But the wolf lives in a hard world, and if there is only food for one, he cannot afford to share. We have already told how he will carry food for many miles to pups that are not his own, and a wolf has been seen to disgorge food in front of a dog that was tied and unable to hunt for itself. The guarding instinct does not extend to water, and two wolves that a moment before have been quarreling over a piece of meat will put their heads together into a pail of water and drink with no sign of conflict.

Although wolves obtain most of their food by killing other animals, their desire for fresh-killed meat can be overemphasized. They have no objection to eating animals found dead, if they are of the right species, even in an area where live prey is common, and they easily acquire the habit of visiting garbage dumps or campgrounds in search of food scraps. When they have made a kill of their own and are unable to eat it all at once they commonly bed down in the vicinity and return at intervals to gnaw on the remains until all useful parts have been taken.

The flesh of the wolf may have served as emergency rations for the early explorers, for whom starvation was not an uncommon hazard. Not only the wolf, but the remains of its food may have been used, according to the following quotation from Alexander Henry, an eighteenth-century fur trader, given by Stanley Young in *The Wolves of North America:*

For breakfast the next morning I put the last square of chocolate into the kettle, and our meal finished we began our march in very indifferent spirits. We were surrounded by large herds of wolves . . . but I carried a gun, and this was our protection. I fired several times, but unfortunately missed at each, for a morsel of wolf flesh would have afforded us a banquet. Our misery, nevertheless, was nearer its end than we imagined. . . . Before sunset we discovered on the ice some remains of the bones of an elk, left there by the wolves. Having instantly gathered them, we encamped, and filling our kettle prepared a meal of strong, excellent soup. The greater part of the night was passed in boiling and regaling on our booty, and early in the morning we felt ourselves strong enough to proceed.

Allowing for probably exaggerated ideas of "large herds of wolves," we can easily believe that similar incidents were not unusual in the early days.

If we judged by what the wolf eats most often we might conclude that it prefers certain prey above others, but it is more likely that availability decides its choice. Where deer and moose are found together, wolves will kill more deer than moose, not because they prefer venison, but because it is easier and less dangerous to kill deer. If beaver are abundant in deer country the wolves will take advantage of this easy food supply and take some pressure off the deer.

Other carnivores, such as foxes, coyotes, cats, dogs, and members of the weasel family are often listed as occasional prey, but there is no evidence that wolves ever hunt these animals in the sense that they hunt their regular prey. We know from firsthand experience in Algonquin Park that they will kill foxes, otters, fishers, and martens, if they are encountered by accident, but we have not seen a case where any of these have been eaten. A few years ago I found a fox which had been caught in a wolf trap and had been killed and pulled out of the trap by two wolves. It was lying a few yards from the trap with no external marks of injury. More recently I skinned a large fisher which had been killed by wolves on a frozen lake. The only mark on it was a clean cut, about two inches long, behind the left shoulder and penetrating into the body cavity. Paul Joslin found a dead marten on a bush road, and the signs showed it had met head on with an adult wolf and a pup and had been caught before it could get off the road. In any of these cases most dogs would have reacted as the wolves did, though perhaps with less efficiency.

The wolf is one of the few mammals that normally kill prey many times larger than themselves. White-tailed deer average twice the weight of a wolf; moose weigh up to twelve times as much. These animals can run at least as fast, their senses are just as keen, and they

are capable of inflicting injury or even death on an attacker. How, then, do wolves manage to kill them regularly?

This question is answered to a large extent in the popular mind by the "myth of the wolf," which pictures the animal as some sort of supernatural monster. More practical minds long ago assumed that wolves must hamstring their large prey by cutting the main tendons in the hind legs. This may happen sometimes by accident, as the wolf commonly attacks from the rear, but neither examination of wolf-killed animals nor field observations indicate that it is a normal part of the wolf's killing technique. The truth is that the wolf is a large wild dog, and not so very large at that. Confronted with the necessity of killing big game for a living and of avoiding injury to itself while doing so, it has evolved a method that brings efficient results.

Wolves traveling the shoreline of a northern lake.

The World of the Wolf

In one of his famous speeches during the Second World War, Winston Churchill spoke of the Italian campaign as an attack on "the soft underbelly of Europe," a method of killing used for centuries by the Japanese in hara-kiri and by wolves in killing deer. Since their killing must be done on the run and they must avoid the sharp hoofs of an animal larger and heavier than themselves, they attack in the practical way and at the most vulnerable spot—the unprotected abdominal region just ahead of the hind legs. One snap of a wolf's jaws in this area will spill a deer's intestines on the ground. It dies quickly, and with no more suffering than in most forms of violent death. From the wolf's standpoint, this is also the shortest route to its favorite food, the internal organs, which are almost always eaten first, with the exception of the stomach, which is not eaten at all. The habit of discarding the stomach of herbivores by the flesh eaters is common, as anyone may learn by watching a cat eat a mouse. The widely circulated story that wolves frequently kill pregnant does for the purpose of obtaining their unborn fawns is unfortunately encouraged by their killing methods. It is extremely doubtful if a wolf would know the condition of a doe before killing it.

This cutting in at an angle from the rear is the standard method used by wolves on animals up to the size of elk, but in the rush and turmoil of trying to stop large prey running at 25 miles an hour or more, they must do the best they can, and it is not surprising if they are not always able to do a neat job. There is no doubt that they will attack at any point they are able to reach. Pimlott has seen two deer that seemed to have been killed by bites on the neck, and Stenlund says, "Usually deer are run down from behind, the wolves biting at the hind flanks and abdomen, or at the flanks and head region simultaneously. Often the deer is knocked to the ground two or three times before it is killed." But it is unusual to find any wounds ahead of the shoulders.

In killing caribou, according to Burkholder, they attack "wherever or whenever the opportunity is presented . . . usually about the neck, shoulder, flank, and hams." When working out the details of a chase in the snow I have sometimes found large bunches of deer hair, pulled out by a wolf as its leap fell short, and an Algonquin Park Ranger, following a chase, picked up the deer's tail, which had been bitten off by its pursuers.

When attacking moose, wolves use essentially the same tactics as for deer, but must accommodate to the moose's size and different reaction to attack. Moose often will not run from wolves, and if a healthy adult moose stands its ground it has no great difficulty repelling even a large pack. On Isle Royale, David Mech was able to watch many encounters

A large bull moose at bay is a formidable opponent, even for a pack of wolves.

between wolves and moose, and of twenty-four observed cases in which the moose defied the wolves, not one was even wounded. The wolves surround their huge intended prey and lunge at it warily in an attempt to excite it to the point of trying to run away, but if it stands fast the wolves give up within five minutes and move on to look for something easier. In one instance, when the wolf pack was still 100 yards away, the moose took the offensive and walked to meet them, but at 30 yards the wolves lost their nerve and left.

When a moose does run, the wolves attack it from the rear, tearing at its hindquarters and legs, even springing on top of its rump, until it weakens from shock and loss of blood and is brought to bay. Even then they do not try to go in for the kill, many generations of wolves having learned that a wounded moose is an extremely dangerous fighter, shooting out its front feet in lightning thrusts with more than enough power to kill a wolf. So they lie down and wait. At this stage the moose often lies down, but then the wolves become active and, by moving in,

Wolf pack chasing a moose. Isle Royale National Park. (David Mech)

cause it to rise again. It may break and run a second or third time, but at last it can run no more and the wolves move closer, sensing the end. In this final stage, when the moose can offer only token defense, there is sometimes much real infighting, with the wolves seizing their prey by the nose, or throat, or any part of its anatomy, until at last it is down to stay.

A moose calf stays with its mother through the first winter. It is by then a big animal, standing up to 5 feet high at the withers and capable of putting up some defense, but it is comparatively vulnerable to an

Wolf pack with moose at bay. Isle Royale National Park. (David Mech)

attack by wolves. It is not unusual for an animal to offer some defense against attack upon its young, but there are few more inspiring examples than that of a cow moose protecting her adolescent offspring against a pack of hungry wolves.

When the wolves appear the cow immediately takes a position at the rear end of the calf, knowing that this is the dangerous point of attack. When they run she runs behind the calf, stopping occasionally to slow down the pursuing wolves. The wolves try hard to separate them, and if they can get the calf even 25 yards from its mother it is usually doomed. When there are twin calves it adds to the difficulty, but the fact that a moose population is able to maintain itself at a constant level in the face of continuous predation suggests that the cows' efforts are often successful.

Wolves do not by any means catch all the moose that try to run away. Many healthy moose are able to outrun wolves, relying on endurance more than speed. In snow up to 2 feet deep, wolves are able to run faster than moose, but in deeper snow the moose's long legs give it the advantage. Wolves are also hampered on rough, thickly grown terrain, and often abandon the chase when a moose enters such an area.

There are several reasons why one animal gets caught and another does not. It may be slowing down because of age, or suffering from disease or from the results of some earlier injury, or it may be just unlucky. For luck affects the animal hunter no less than the human, and an impassable windfall or an unexpected drop-off over a ledge may cause either the hunter or the hunted to break its stride and make the difference between life and death. I have seen several examples of this kind of bad luck to white-tailed deer being chased by wolves. Considering the marked variation in temperament of individual animals, it may well be that even with equal physical capabilities one would be easier to catch than another. Studies in Algonquin Park have shown that, except in summer, the majority of deer killed by wolves are in the five-year-and-over-class. It is not surprising that animals best able to avoid wolves

Moose calf approximately two months old. Wolves can catch them readily at this age. (Newfoundland Dept. of Agriculture, Mines and Resources)

come from the most active period of life, roughly corresponding to the eighteen-to-forty group in human beings. The high incidence of fawns in summer kills provides additional evidence of selectivity according to availability, as fawns would certainly be the easiest of deer to catch.

105

Caribou are the principal prey of tundra wolves. (Newfoundland Dept. of Agriculture, Mines and Resources)

Opposite page: Tundra wolves migrate long distances to follow caribou to their winter range.

Caribou bull during the rut. (Newfoundland Dept. of Agriculture, Mines and Resources)

A good example of the relationship between disease and predation is provided by the condition known as hydatid disease, a rather common affliction of moose. This is caused by a small kind of tapeworm, *Echinococcus granulosus,* the adults of which often occur in large numbers in the intestinal tracts of wolves. The eggs are transferred in the droppings of wolves to vegetation, which is eaten by moose, and the incomplete or larval state is passed in cysts within the moose, most frequently in the lungs. Each of these cysts, or hydatids, which commonly reach 2 inches in diameter, and are often much larger, contains thousands of immature tapeworms, and more than a hundred cysts have been found in the lungs of a single moose. When wolves eat an infected moose they also eat the cysts, and the tapeworms develop into adults within the wolf, thus completing the cycle. This is indeed a fascinating chain of events, because the parasite depends for its perpetuation on

107

infected moose being eaten by wolves, and by heavily infecting moose it renders them more likely to be eaten.

Since it is possible for man to become infected with hydatid disease, and his most likely source of infection would be dogs, which also harbor the adult tapeworms, dogs should never be allowed to eat the internal organs of moose. This tapeworm also occurs in deer, caribou, elk, and reindeer, but in Ontario it is by far the most common in moose. It does not seem to have any disabling effect on wolves, but a heavy infection may cause enteritis.

Although wolves "select" weaker animals by testing them in the chase, there is reason to think that inferior animals sometimes betray themselves, and it seems probable that, over the ages, wolves have become highly sensitive to signs of weakness. W. A. Fuller, of the Canadian Wildlife Service, tells of watching a pack of wolves approach four bison in Wood Buffalo National Park, but only one of the bison showed concern, and it was obviously a partly crippled animal. Lois Crisler writes that a band of caribou being chased "runs as if it were one object with many legs," but that the one animal that is eventually caught "loses the speed of the band almost immediately," and may veer off on a course of its own.

Wolves definitely like to attack their prey on the run, a point well illustrated in their hunting of moose, and there is some reason to think that even smaller animals might sometimes avoid being killed if they chose to stand their ground. There are cases on record of single caribou, elk, white-tailed deer, and Dall sheep frustrating wolves by failing to run away. According to old records, as reported by Young in *The Wolves of North America,* the tendency to panic made the horse an easy prey in spite of its size and strength. As described in one account, "Instead of stopping and bravely fighting off the bloodthirsty beasts, they would run. Then the whole pack were sure to leave the bolder animals and make for the runaways."

Opportunities to judge the relative speeds of wolves and their prey are rare. Young says that a wolf has been "clocked" at 28 miles an hour for 200 yards. Stenlund reports a wolf chased by a car on a frozen lake and making "35 to 40 for 4 miles." Rue gives the speed of the white-tailed deer as 30 to 35 miles an hour for short distances. Murie and Crisler agree that caribou can run faster than wolves. Cowan was satisfied that moose, elk, and mule deer were all able to run faster than a wolf. I have taken careful measurements of the tracks made by a white-tailed deer and a wolf during a chase on ground lightly covered by snow, with good footing for both animals. The leaps of the deer averaged 15 feet, those of the wolf 12 feet, but the rate of leaping may have been different. The wolf did not catch the deer in a half-mile chase. I think all this adds up to the fact that speed is only one factor, and perhaps not the most important one, in the catching of prey by wolves.

In order to maintain a balance between predator and prey, neither can have a great advantage over the other. Under natural conditions and without the restraint of predation, deer would increase to the point of destroying their own habitat. But if they were too easy to catch, the wolves would kill too many and reduce the population to a point where reproduction would be unable to keep ahead of predation. As it is, by working hard all the time the wolves make a good living, and hold the deer population to a number that balances with the food supply. As Murie says of caribou and wolves, "It is hard to know how 'nip and tuck' the relationships are between the two species. A predator's ability to catch its prey must balance with the prey's ability to escape."

It is a common belief that wolves are able to kill deer or other game whenever they want to, but this is far from true. We may know how many deer are killed by wolves in a given area, but very little about the ones that got away. A European study of predatory birds showed that of 688 attempts to kill, only 7.6 per cent were successful. Mech found that the Isle Royale wolves were able to kill only six moose out of seventy-seven tries, a hunting success of 7.8 per cent.

No such study has been made of the wolf's hunting of any other prey,

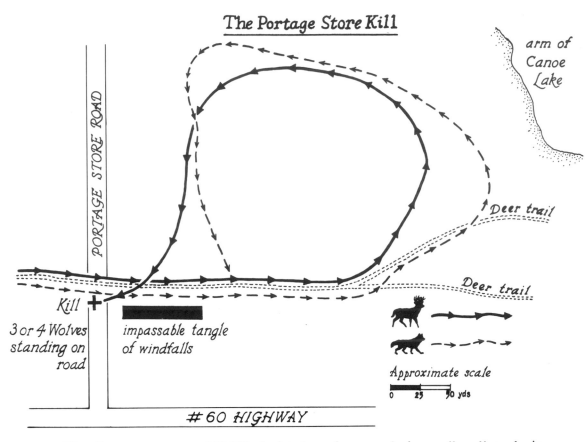

The Portage Store Kill

The diagrams on pages 110-113 depict deer chases made by small wolf packs in Algonquin Park as deduced from tracks in the snow by R. J. Rutter. (Diagrams by Paul Geraghty)

but enough has been seen of its attempts against white-tailed deer, caribou, and mountain sheep to suggest a similar ratio of success to failure. Several diagrams are included in these pages of chases that I followed through in Algonquin Park, illustrating typical kill patterns of white-tailed deer, and all of these chases are short. Although Young makes such curious statements as "The hunting technique of wolves is based on the exhaustion of its prey," and "The explanation lies in the wolf's great endurance," there is general agreement among many observers that, with the exception of moose, which require a special approach, wolves depend largely upon a sudden dash and a short chase. Crisler records one chase of caribou that went nearly 5 miles, and Mech saw one 3-mile chase after moose, but these are exceptions.

The Pewee Lake Kill

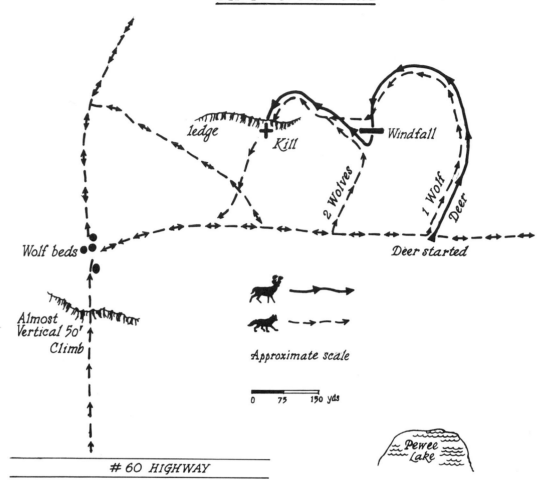

The diagrams are intended to illustrate several aspects of a wolf's hunting, such as the possible use of strategy, the taking advantage of a deer's habit of running in a circle, the importance of luck. It should be emphasized, however, that there has not been enough of this kind of work done to allow us to say to what extent some of these apparent features may be mere coincidence. The diagrams show that they *do* happen.

In the Portage Store kill the pack consisted of five or six, and they had apparently been running in single file behind the deer as far as the road. I do not know if the lead wolf was far in advance of the others, but it was the only one that followed the deer across the road. Why did

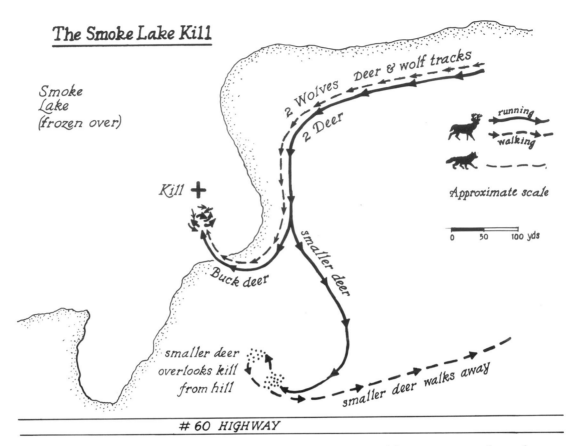

The Smoke Lake Kill

Smoke
Lake
(frozen over)

2 Wolves   Deer & wolf tracks

2 Deer

Kill +

smaller deer

Buck deer

running

walking

Approximate scale

0   50   100 yds

smaller deer
overlooks kill
from hill

smaller deer walks away

60 HIGHWAY

the others stop and wait at that point? Everything suggests that the single wolf was trying to turn the deer, and when it cut off to its left, with an extra burst of speed, just before completing the circle, there seems to be only one logical explanation—it was preventing the deer from turning left and going around the same trail again. Whether or not the deer knew the wolves were waiting on the road, it had no choice but to turn right, because straight ahead was a rock ledge covered with fallen trees, quite impassable to any large animal.

In the Pewee Lake kill we have another circular run, and again an unexpected obstacle played a part in the outcome. The deer could not see what was beyond the snow-covered windfall that it jumped over, and the two wolves that it met face to face probably were as surprised as the deer. But at this point the deer had to make a quick turn and then scramble up a rough slope, and it lost enough ground to make the difference. Even then it might have escaped if it hadn't blundered

112

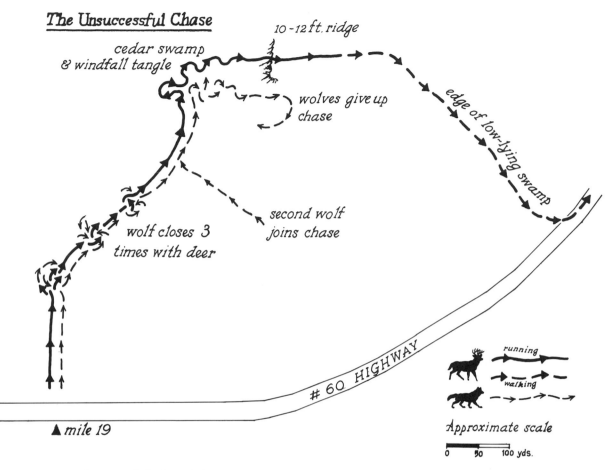

The Unsuccessful Chase

10 - 12 ft. ridge

cedar swamp & windfall tangle

wolves give up chase

edge of low-lying swamp

second wolf joins chase

wolf closes 3 times with deer

60 HIGHWAY

▲ mile 19

running

walking

Approximate scale

0   50   100 yds.

over that rock ledge. The wonder is, considering the odds against them, not that the deer are caught, but that they are able to avoid being caught for so long. I suspect the answer is that the odds against them are not nearly so great as they seem to be. The ability of the deer to escape *almost* balances with the wolves' ability to catch them.

The Smoke Lake kill is a simple illustration of how quickly a deer may be killed if it runs out on to a frozen lake. There were only two wolves involved and they chased two deer parallel to the lake shore until the smaller deer turned and ran up a hill and the other, a large buck, ran out on the ice. Snow was about 3 feet deep in the bush, and the wolves could do nothing but run along behind the plunging deer. My notebook of the time gives the following description: "The holes in the snow where the deer had been running were big enough to bury a man. There were handfuls of hair along this furious trail but no blood."

There was much less snow on the lake, and the wolves appeared to have made a desperate sprint as soon as they hit the ice, stopping the buck in less than 50 yards.

The action of the smaller deer of running up the hill and then turning back to watch the struggle below was interesting. Stenlund describes a case in which a wolf chased a fawn within 50 feet of a standing deer which behaved as an "uninterested bystander."

The diagram of the unsuccessful chase, only one of several I have followed, shows how the stubborn persistance of a vigorous deer can defeat the best efforts of a wolf. In this case a single wolf brought the deer to bay three times, but each time the deer was able to stand it off and go on. By the time the second wolf joined the chase, the deer had reached an area so cluttered by fallen logs and thick-standing brush that the wolves were much handicapped and soon gave up. There was two feet of slightly packed snow and the wolves were sinking only about four inches, although the running deer went right to the ground on each jump. This accounts for the wolf's being able to catch up with the deer so readily, but that was not enough. Had there been a pack scattered over the territory the result could have been different, although in another case I followed the trail of a single wolf chasing a deer for a mile through an area being worked by a pack, and the deer got away. This was luck again, for none of the pack happened to be in the right place at the right time.

It was pointed out early in this book that it was an advantage to wolves to hunt in packs, because they hunted prey larger than themselves, and the probability of several wolves making a kill was greater than that of one wolf. Whether or not a pack uses any strategy beyond mere numbers is not an easy question to answer. Early writing on wolves usually took it for granted that they did and stated as fact that wolves organized their hunting efforts with military precision. I am suspicious of these early tales, because they are seldom documented and because they make such a good story. It was much easier and more convenient to believe them than to test their truth.

More recent and more objective wolf studies do not give much support to the idea. Lois Crisler watched two wolf-caribou hunts, both involving the same two wolves, in which one wolf stayed behind while the other went past the caribou and then drove it back toward its partner. This plan, if it was a plan, did not result in a kill or even a near kill. Stenlund tells of two cases reported to him, one occurring on an island and the other on a point projecting into a lake. In both cases part of a wolf pack went through the wooded point or island while the rest went around the outside and intercepted deer driven into the open. It is not stated whether this was seen or deduced from tracks, but in either case it would be difficult to decide whether or not it involved deliberate strategy. It may have just happened that some wolves went through the bush and some around the outside, or the wolves may have been only using a method of travel that had brought results before and which they now followed automatically.

This last could also apply to those times when a single wolf chases a deer that runs in a circle and is caught by other pack members. A deer I was once tracking made a complete circle until it intersected my trail. If a wolf pack had been strung out behind the deer it would have run right into them. This kind of thing could account for part of the apparent strategy in the diagramed kill on the Portage Store Road.

In Mech's study of wolves and moose, although the wolves followed a regular pattern in their hunting, there was nothing that could be called strategy. Murie watched many chases of both caribou and mountain sheep but did not see anything to suggest a preconceived plan. Two wolves I was trailing in Algonquin Park jumped two deer which ran in opposite directions, with a wolf after each. This was anything but co-operation, and neither deer was caught.

Wolves do use different tactics for different kinds of prey, no doubt arrived at by trial and error over a long period. Their hunting of deer

Although it is not known which of the senses is most important to wolves, they do make good use of their noses when following tracks or searching for a buried bone.

and moose has already been described. In mountain country, where they hunt elk and mountain sheep, they have learned to travel the high ridges so that they can charge these animals from above, as a wolf is at a great disadvantage running uphill. With caribou, which are of the open country and very fast runners, their best weapon is persistence, and they simply chase the caribou about until they find one they can catch. This seems to have been essentially their tactics for hunting bison on the open plains.

There is considerable evidence that they do use such simple devices as ambushing, heading off, and trying to knock an animal off its feet, but all these may be seen among playful dogs and are probably instinctive in many hunting animals.

It is an open question which of the senses—sight, scent, or hearing—is the most important to the wolf in locating its prey. We are so accustomed to the educated noses of hunting dogs that we are likely to take for granted the same characteristic in wolves. Again we must turn to David Mech for the only quantitative evidence on the subject. He observed that wolves became aware of moose more often when they were upwind, but not uncommonly failed to detect upwind moose, and sometimes "sensed" them on a cross- or downwind. In the latter cases, if they decided to test the moose, they generally circled until they could approach it from the downwind side. It should be noted that Mech's observations were made from an airplane, so there was no way of knowing that the wolves could not sometimes hear moose. A feeding moose, pulling down and breaking off branches, might be heard for quite a long distance.

Murie does not express an opinion on the subject but tells how he was often able to approach very close to resting wolves without being detected. He thought they might be more alert in places where they were hunted, and comments, "When alert their keen eyes do not miss much." He records one observation of a wolf finding a caribou calf by following its very fresh tracks. S. I. Ognev, in *Mammals of the U.S.S.R.*

117

Fishers frequently live as scavengers off animals that have been killed by wolves. (Ont. Dept. of Lands & Forests)

and Adjacent Countries, writes of wolves, "Hearing is the most highly developed sense; senses of sight and smell being markedly less well developed."

Whether it hunts with its nose or not, there is no doubt that the wolf has a sensitive and educated nose at close range. Every new object is carefully sniffed all over, and any really "exotic" scents, such as old motor oil, paint, or any kind of perfume receive special attention. On the other hand, the habit of "testing the air" with its nose, so common in many animals, is not noticeable in a wolf. It does carry its head high and fixes anything in which it is interested with a penetrating stare. This is a matter for investigation.

A belief that wolves kill wantonly for the love of killing is well established in wolf mythology, but examples of wasteful killing are lacking in modern wolf research. The Ontario Department of Lands and Forests reports that in a seven-year Wolf Research Program in Algonquin Park it found 70 per cent of white-tailed deer killed by wolves completely consumed and the remainder utilized in varying

Wolves will return to old kills to dig up bones that they have buried.

degrees. Leftovers from kills were eaten by carnivores other than wolves, some of which depend to a significant extent on this food source during the winter. My own records of animals using wolf kills include the raven, gray jay, fox, fisher, marten, and flying squirrel. Both golden and bald eagles occur in Algonquin Park in winter, although neither is found there at other seasons, and their food while there is derived almost entirely from wolf kills.

Not enough research has yet been done to allow positive conclusions on why wolves sometimes consume their prey completely and at other times leave much of it uneaten. Stenlund found in his Minnesota study that "when deer were more plentiful in the region, wolves often ate only the internal organs or a single ham and then traveled on. During recent years, with deer less numerous, carcasses are cleaned up so that only pieces of hide, head, large leg bones, and paunch are left." Abundance of prey is quite likely a factor in utilization, but there are others of equal importance, such as the number of wolves involved. With a pack of eight or ten there is not likely to be underutilization, as there would

119

be little left of an average deer after they had all eaten. But when the two wolves killed the buck on Smoke Lake they ate only a quarter of it, and the rest served as a feeding station for smaller animals all winter. In a case like this the wolf's inherent instinct to travel may well be a factor. Two wolves could not eat a whole deer, and if these two were traveling at the time they might not happen to come that way again.

Wolves and dogs have many things in common. They have strong similarities in physical structure and behavior, and they interbreed readily, producing fertile offspring. One striking difference is that dogs may breed in any season, but wolves are restricted to a period of not more than two months in the winter of each year.

They are sexually mature at the end of their second year, and there are several cases on record of both males and females mating successfully at that age. This does not mean that they always breed at two years, however, as there is some evidence that younger wolves may be prevented from mating by competition from older animals.

Finally even the large leg bones of a deer are carried away and eaten.

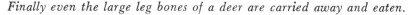

Fall and Winter

In Algonquin Park, Ontario, breeding activity is noticeable through February and March, probably reaching its peak about the end of February. Contrary to popular accounts of special "mating howls," we have not heard any sounds that seem to be directly connected with the breeding season. All available information suggests that mating takes place within the pack without any marked disturbance of the established social organization, but with a lot of added excitement.

I don't know who started the widely circulated story that wolves mate for life, but I suspect it is in the same class as the one about their elaborate hunting strategy. It would be impossible—or has been to date—to obtain such information on wild wolves, so a positive statement cannot be made one way or the other. In the only recorded case I know of in which an identifiable pair was watched for two years, the same animals did stay together, and it is quite possible that this is usual, barring accidents. It has been found that captive wolves do not always keep the same mate, and are far from being strictly monogamous. Two males may mate with the same female and one male with two females. This sort of thing might be expected of an animal as socially inclined as the wolf, and should be thought of in relation to the manner in which the whole pack joins in caring for the young.

The established social order of a wolf pack, which has already been described, has a profound effect on mating activities, and it seems quite possible that it is one of the factors affecting the "biological control" that regulates wolf populations. In a small pack, perhaps containing only two or three animals of breeding age, there might be no difficulty, but in a large pack the conflict of social status and choice of mates causes much temporary confusion. Wolves are quite choosy in selecting mating partners, and mutual preference is not common. It may work out something like this:

Female A is interested in male B, but B rejects her in favor of female C, who is trying to win the favor of male D, who is the dominant wolf of the pack. D, however, is set on female E, a pretty little peripheral wolf with no social standing. D exercises his dominant position to prevent male B from courting female C, and at the same time his attention is divided further between his interest in female E and upholding his position as No. 1 wolf. Female C prevents female E from accepting D, but female A is dominant over female C and interferes with her advances to D.

It can happen that while D is absorbed in maintaining his dominant position over everybody, some other male mates with E, and she may be the only one that manages to have pups. In spite of this humiliating situation, D will likely maintain his No. 1 social position and when the pups arrive will take his place as the head of the family, a father in name only. A situation similar to this took place among George Wilson's wolves in St. Louis in the spring of 1964.

By the first of April the mating instinct has been completely submerged for another year, and the pack can settle down to its routine of traveling, hunting, eating, and sleeping. By the middle of the month the ice on the lakes has turned to watery slush and the streams to channels of ice water. Bush travel becomes greatly restricted for both wolves and men—often impossible for the latter—and there is not much contact between the two during spring breakup. Hunting must become very much a game of chance for the wolves, with the odds changing by the hour.

When the temperature drops during the night, the wet snow hardens and footing becomes miraculously good, best of all if there is a light fall of new snow to cushion the surface. But when a mild day follows a cold night, as it often does, then before noon the surface, although it still appears firm, will scarcely support a rabbit. Bush men describe this condition by saying that "the bottom has fallen out of the snow," and this is just what happens. The unpacked snow beneath thaws first, and the whole thing caves in if any pressure is applied on top.

During this freezing-thawing period there are often indications of extensive wandering by wolves in the early part of the day, and other animals also take advantage of the good footing. Deer are tempted to spread out from their winter concentration areas while the going is good, and the snowshoe rabbit will turn up at places where it is not found throughout all the rest of the year. Whether the wolves kill more rabbits at such times, or vary their diet from the usual proportions in any way, is not known, but we have found no evidence that they do. If they have a hard time getting around, the deer are equally handicapped.

This is the season when the water that has risen above the lake ice freezes into a glassy sheet that provides no footing for either wolves or deer. Sometimes a deer does go out on glare ice, and when it does it generally falls and is quite helpless. Wolves kill deer under these circumstances, but probably with just as much difficulty as when the ice is covered by snow. David Mech watched wolves traveling on ice a good deal around Isle Royale, and noted that they were very reluctant to walk on glare ice and would go considerably out of their way to avoid it.

It is during this in-between season that the pregnant females establish dens in which to bear their young. Very little is known about this phase of wolf life history. Is the den site decided upon and made ready far in advance? Since the activities of the whole pack will be centered on the denning area for at least two months, is its location left entirely to the prospective mother? Do the wolves really make extra kills within easy reach of the den and leave them uneaten to insure a food supply for the new family? We at least have an opinion on the last question. We don't think they do. For certainty, we can only repeat what we said earlier—"The young are born in a den in the spring."

The Voice of the Wolf

ONE OF THE most interesting things about a wolf is its howl, but in the past this only served to increase man's antagonism toward the animal. "They go in droves by night, with dismal yelling cries," wrote Mark Catesby in 1743, and similar references are common in the early records. To a pioneer farmer who had just lost a dozen sheep or a fat calf, the howl of a wolf must have sounded like adding insult to injury.

In those days it was necessary to take the wolf seriously as a competitor for the available meat supply, but that situation no longer exists. Elsewhere in this book Doug Pimlott discusses man's past, present, and possible future relations with wolves, and it is clear from the evidence that today they offer no significant threat to our economic interests or personal safety anywhere in the world.

Having eliminated the wolf as a serious competitor, it was a long time before we began to think of it as anything more than a disagreeable outlaw, but when we did we soon learned that it was an animal with a wide range of interesting characteristics about which we knew very little. This chapter is a summary of what we know of the wolf as a vocalist.

It is unfortunate that the word "howl" must be used to describe the wolf's voice, because of its unfavorable associations. Actually, wolf howls have a remarkably clear tone, and if we can listen to them without prejudice we will find that musically they rank far ahead of many sounds of nature that we have learned to enjoy. John Theberge, who was among the first to apply electronics to howl analysis, says they could be described better as singing, as their harmonic structure is similar to that of the human voice or of musical instruments.

Of all the questions wolf research has been trying to answer, the apparently simple one, "Why do wolves howl?" has proved to be among the most difficult. It is hard to convince people that the howling of wolves does not mean something—that they are chasing a deer, or killing one, or calling up reinforcements, or warning human listeners that it is time to climb a tree. When forms were distributed among campers in Algonquin Park, on which they were asked to record any wolf experiences, they sent in reports like the following: "The wolves were closing in on a deer about a mile north of us. They must have caught it, as they all howled together and then were quiet." The fact is, there is no evidence that wolves howl during a chase, while they are making a kill, or afterward.

If it is difficult to believe that wolves do not howl when they are in pursuit of prey, it seems even more incredible that the wild, spine-tingling clamor of a wolf pack in full voice does not scare the daylights out of all other animals. Nevertheless, there is nothing to indicate that other animals react to the howling of wolves any differently from the way they do to other normal sounds of the forest. On one occasion I had an amplifier on the roof of a car and was broadcasting recorded wolf howls. One of the semitame highway deer, feeding nearby, walked casually toward the car while the howl was in progress, looking for the usual handout of food. Murie writes of wolves and caribou,

More than 200 cows and calves came out above the East Fork wolf den. They were strung out in a long straggly line, feeding as they moved. A wolf howled from a short distance above the caribou and soon its howls were answered by two or three wolves at the den. Although the caribou were between the lone wolf and those at the den, they continued feeding. I could not see that any of them heeded the howling.

There is no reason to think that deer or other animals associate the sound of wolves' howling with danger.

125

Replying to the howl of a pack.

A wolf howl is not the unique sound that many accounts would have us believe. Although one of the many descriptions cited in *The Wolves of North America* says it is a sound "entirely unlike that made by any other living creature; a prolonged, deep, wailing howl, perhaps the most dismal sound ever heard by human ear," the voices of the wolf and of the dog stand in about the same relation to each other as the tracks of the two animals. There are differences that may be described, but they are of a general nature, and neither can be identified with certainty merely by looking or listening.

A mental picture of a howling wolf derived from popular lore might be of an animal on a stark hilltop on a cold, moonlit winter night. This is very romantic, but it has already been pointed out that the best howling time is in the pleasant days of fall, and the wolf is as likely to be in the middle of a swamp as on a hilltop. It may be sitting, standing, lying, or walking about. Perhaps standing is the most common howling position, but they frequently howl while lying down, and not very often sitting, probably because a wolf does not sit nearly as much as a dog.

The Voice of the Wolf

In a pack howl there may be a good deal of milling, when the animals walk up and down and weave in and out among themselves. The tail may be hanging loosely in a normal position or it may be stiffened and straight out behind, depending on the degree of excitement. A wolf's tail is one of its most expressive members, and a tail carried high usually means an aggressive high-status animal. Tail-wagging, as an expression of pleasure or good will, is a characteristic shared by dogs, foxes, and wolves. Murie reports seeing a wolf wagging its tail when hunting mice, and tame wolves sometimes wag their tails while joining in a friendly howl.

One habit in which we may observe consistency if not purpose is that of spontaneous group howling in the evening and to a lesser extent in the early morning. Murie watched a pack leaving for the night's hunt

The position of the head varies with the type of howl.

Charge — adult wolves playing. The high tail indicates an aggressive, high-status animal.

Running at full speed on crusted snow. Note the high tail.

many times, and they commonly made something of a social affair of the occasion, including a pack howl. One of my first howling experiences was from a camp on Bailey Lake in Algonquin Park, when a pack howled at eight o'clock in the evening and at exactly eight the next morning, each time from the same place.

Pack or group howling is not a haphazard affair. It is initiated by one wolf, not necessarily the pack leader, but the animal with the most active inclination to howl at that time. As each wolf comes in, it is at a different pitch, possibly by design, but probably only because each has a different voice range. This produces the wild harmony which once heard is never forgotten. All sorts of odd variations may be heard. There may be one wolf with a voice noticeably lower than the others, keeping up a droning obligato throughout the howl; another may introduce a tremolo effect, as though the tongue were vibrating in the mouth; another may come up with a very high note, like a singer reaching for a high C. Usually the performance lasts about thirty seconds, but sometimes it runs on for a minute, and not uncommonly it dies down and then picks up again. It most often just fades away, but may stop very abruptly, sometimes to the accompaniment of a sharp bark from one of the wolves.

It has not yet been discovered how many notes may be produced by one wolf, but each has its own voice, which may be anywhere from a deep bass to a high tenor. As far as we know, the size or sex of a wolf has no relation to its voice. Individual howls seldom last longer than five seconds, but can go much longer. When a wolf howls it shapes its mouth carefully and usually closes its eyes.

That wolves take their howling seriously and that it really takes something out of them is indicated by the fact that after they have had a good howl it is generally difficult to get them to howl again until a lapse of a half hour or more. If they do howl more than once, the howls grow progressively weaker and less enthusiastic. A curious point here is that this does not usually apply to individual animals. A wolf howling by

129

itself will often answer an indefinite number of times, and this again emphasizes the fact that there is a lot more to a pack howl than a group of individuals howling at the same time.

If there is any message conveyed by group howling, it is probably connected with territory. Many animals utter vocal sounds on what they consider to be their home territory, apparently as a warning to possible rivals that it is already occupied. The singing of male birds on their nesting territory is the outstanding example. With wolves we have to consider that they appear to enjoy howling together; it seems to relieve tensions and express a general feeling of well-being. Whether their more or less regular morning and evening howling is intended for others or simply serves some function of pack organization is debatable.

My thinking on the subject is influenced by the experience of howling *with* wolves instead of *at* them. All studies of animal behavior are impeded by our inability to enter into the animal's world. By howling with wolves it is possible to break down that barrier and, for perhaps a half minute, literally become a wolf. For several years now, whenever conditions were right, I have joined in a pack howl with the captive wolves at the Wildlife Research Station. The observed reactions of the wolves, and my own very strong feeling at such times that we were all howling together simply because we were glad to be together, have led me to believe that the *spontaneous* group howling of wolves is entirely subjective; that it has no meaning and is not intended to have any meaning except to the animals themselves.

It is true that wolves are stimulated by certain sounds, and if they are stimulated enough they will howl, unless there are suppressing factors greater than the stimulation. An example of this would be howling too close to the wolves, when their natural fear and suspicion of man would be greater than their inclination to howl. One very dark night when we stopped to howl on the highway in Algonquin Park, it turned out there was a pack just over a hundred yards away across a small marsh on an old railway embankment. After our howl we could hear them whining and giving an occasional subdued yelp, but we were just a little too near for them to concentrate on howling. There is nothing remarkable about getting so close to wolves. I have stood within 60 feet of a wild wolf and talked quietly to it for a half minute before it walked casually away.

Wolves have been known to answer many sounds besides real or artificial howls, and they need not resemble anything that could be mistaken for a wolf's voice. A friend of mine had an excellent response to a tape recording of a lively excerpt from grand opera, and I have had good results with an army bugle and from a recording of trumpets of the U. S. Marines. John Theberge tells how a pack which was often stimulated by a recorder carried in a truck learned to howl at the slamming of the truck door, or even simply by the sound of the truck stopping at the usual place. Another time and with another pack a wrong connection in the recorder caused "an intense high-frequency note," and the wolves answered at once. All of which means that the howl of a wolf has no simple explanation.

My personal opinion is that the strict language of science will never be adequate to explain completely a wolf's howl. Any explanation will have to be tinged with anthropomorphism. Last year, in an article in

The howling of one wolf does not always stimulate the others to howl.

the Department of Lands and Forests publication *The Raven,* John Theberge wrote, "The method of science is objective. It can observe and relate facts, but it cannot speculate or surmise." This was in an article on wolf-howling. But the late Aldo Leopold, who could hardly be accused of being an unscientific naturalist, said years ago, "Only a mountain has lived long enough to listen objectively to the howl of a wolf." If we are unable to speculate or surmise we will not get very far in our studies of the meaning of wolf howls.

There is a difference between wolf-howling and wolf-listening. In the first we initiate the action by either howling with the human voice or by playing amplified records of wolf howls, thus hoping to induce any wolves within hearing to answer. This is chiefly useful for locating wolves and has been used to find their dens and rendezvous and, to some extent, to trace their movements. A basic weakness in the method, so far as behavior studies go, is that as soon as you howl, an unnatural situation is introduced. You may learn something of what the wolves do after you locate them, but you can't be sure that their behavior is what it would have been if you had not howled. In wolf-listening you simply place yourself in wolf territory and wait for the wolves to howl. In this way you do not find as many wolves, but you are reasonably sure that neither their howling nor their movements are influenced by your actions. The howls produced by the first method may be called "stimulated," by the second, "spontaneous."

A wolf pup practicing a howl. (E. C. Walsh)

The Voice of the Wolf

Back in 1956, when I first began to take more than a casual interest in wolves, I was attracted by the references in wolf stories to "mating howls," "lonesome howls," "rallying howls," and stories of how wolves howled back and forth in order to keep in touch while hunting. Somehow, I doubted that these writers knew as much about the meaning of wolf howls as they professed to, and as I lived in Huntsville, Ontario, only 25 miles from Algonquin Provincial Park, noted for its good wolf population, there seemed to be no good excuse for not doing my own listening. So I got together with my friend and fellow townsman Abbott Conway, and we formed what we called "The Huntsville Wolf-Listeners," with the object of listening to wolves as much as possible, learning when and where they might be listened to, and finding out what we could about wolves in general, including why they howled.

We established an area of operations at Shanty Lake, an isolated corner without roads or canoe routes and not cluttered by fishermen or hikers. Our decision to use this place was encouraged by an experience which Abbott had had near there a year before, and it proved to be a fortunate choice. Abbott's adventure was a good example of what may happen when a man meets wolves for the first time. This is what he told me:

"It was in the late fall of 1955, and the first snow was lying on the ground to a depth of two or three inches. I drove up to the Park to survey the trail leading through the 'back door' in to Booth Lake and McCarthy Creek.

"I walked in the Half-way House road to the phone line and then followed the line north to where it forks between the Shanty Lake turn and Raja Lake. When I reached the fork I went to the left and had gone only two or three hundred yards when the howl began.

"It started with a long, low howl, almost a moaning sound, and then began to rise higher and higher. Other wolves joined in with that curious off-key effect that we now know so well, until the sound seemed to fill the whole bush. There seemed to be three successive fallings and

133

Eyes open when deer flies buzz too close.

risings of the sound, and these produced a pattern that seemed to shift to every direction. At the time I was not used to listening to wolves and it seemed to be impossible to make a true bearing on the direction of the sound. It seemed to ebb and flow, but one distinct impression I recall was that at times it sounded as though the pack was running down the trail toward me in full cry! I did not know much about wolves then and my impressions were different than they would be today. I felt a bit like a Russian peasant, and was prepared to take to the trees at any moment.

"I have no doubt that it scared the devil out of me, but by the time I had retreated as far as the fork I had cooled down, and I forced myself to stay there and eat my lunch before starting out for the highway."

Our experiences with the Shanty Lake wolves suggest that our camp, near the ruins of an ancient lumber shanty on the north shore of the lake, lies just within the southwest boundary of their territory, and a pack from further west comes over for a visit periodically. I think the Huntsville Wolf-Listeners have turned up some observations at this site on wolf movements and the possible meaning of certain howling patterns that are worth placing on record.

For instance, on February 2, 1957, Abbott Conway and I bedded down in the snow with our campfire backed against a big pine log near the Beaver Ponds, one of the complex of ponds and lakes in our Shanty Lake territory. It was cloudy and very dark with a few flakes of snow falling.

We were absorbing the last of many bowls of tea before turning in at eight o'clock when a tremendous, deep-toned single wolf howl rolled out of the darkness from the east. This was followed by two or three deep barks, then another long howl, and that was all. We can't say what happened while we were in our sleeping bags, but at seven o'clock in the morning there was a good pack howl, which seemed to come from the same place as the single of the evening.

We were on a limited time schedule and did not go in that direction,

Scratching an itchy ear.

but went south to intersect Wolf Creek, which was our route to the highway. Here we found tracks of four wolves that had been made during the night, coming up the frozen creek from the direction of the howling we had heard. We followed them for a mile, until they swung off to the east.

We read the signs to mean that these wolves had come from where we heard the single howl and their night hunting had taken them in a wide circle leading back to the starting point, where we heard them howl in the morning.

This deep, single howl with a few barks is described perfectly in *The Wolves of North America,* where it is said to be "a call for assembling a group of wolves." We have heard it only twice, both times in the Shanty Lake area, which brings up the possibility of its being a characteristic of a particular wolf. Each time, however, the pattern of activity was so clear that we suspect it is one of the few known wolf calls to which we can attach a special meaning.

The other time was in the fall of the same year, 1957, and we were camped in the old clearing at Shanty Lake. At 8:20 in the evening a pack howled from the north, up around Raja Lake, about a mile away. Before they had quite finished, the deep-voiced single broke in, about a half mile from us to the northeast. It was a beautiful bass howl, again divided in the middle by several guttural barks. Only twenty minutes later the whole pack broke into an exceptionally animated howl from the position of the single.

The picture here seemed even more clear. The single wolf held an influential position in this pack; it may have gone off on an independent

The curled-up position gives good protection from flies.

hunt during the day, or it may have become separated the night before. The pack and the single had bedded down a half mile apart, perhaps both uncertain of the exact location of the other. The pack gave its usual evening howl; the single answered at once. The fact that the pack moved to the single was an indication of its dominant position. Jerry Woolpy noted that in Brookfield Zoo the dominant animal was "the principal object of affection by the rest of the pack."

One other distinctive individual howl which seems to be meaningful for the wolf uttering it, but does not seem to serve any particular purpose, is what we refer to as the "lonesome howl." This is a rising and falling sound—a crescendo-decrescendo—and is sometimes given by a wolf that is left alone or is separated from its usual company. At times there is a variation in which the opening crescendo is left off and the howl starts high and slides down to die away on a low note. Once I visited Dagwood when he had been isolated for howling experiments and had been alone all day. He was so starved for company that he "cried" all the time I was there, and when I left and was not long out of sight he gave this "falling" howl some half dozen times.

In the following wolf-listening and wolf-howling experience the lonesome howl seemed to be used in a different way. We were in our camp on the north side of Shanty Lake at the end of October. We had arrived late and it was well after dark by the time we made camp and had supper. We had heard no wolves.

Then, at nine o'clock a single wolf with a very deep voice howled—just a straight howl—from the east end of the lake, only a little more than a quarter mile from our campfire. A second wolf then howled from near the same place, and this one gave the up-and-down lonesome call. It had a particularly ringing, pleasant voice, and Abbott, who likes to name things, at once christened it Mello-bell; the other he appropriately called Basso-profundo. Names are a great convenience in keeping records, and for further help we thought of Mello-bell as a female and Basso as a male.

The Voice of the Wolf

These two wolves alternated their curiously distinctive howls from the same place for five or ten minutes, then fell silent. About a half hour later Mello-bell howled from the south side of the lake and Basso answered from away over to the east; they had moved off in opposite directions. Not long afterward Mello-bell was around at the west end of the lake and Basso was quite distant in the east, and we went to bed.

In the morning all was quiet, but I had a portable tape recorder with taped howls, and at breakfast I turned it on without connecting the amplifier. We were rather startled to get an immediate response from what sounded like three wolves, just off the east end of the lake on Wolf Creek. This sounded like three pups, but it is hard to be sure at that time of year, when pup voices are just maturing. We did not bother them again, but to our further surprise, at nine o'clock Mello-bell started her lonesome howl from the northwest; she was still traveling in a circle, and must have heard the pups howl. This time I answered her vocally, and we howled back and forth for a half hour, when she tired of the game.

We purposely stayed away from Wolf Creek all day, not wishing to disturb the situation, and did not use the "howler" in the evening. Just at dark Basso-profundo howled from far away in the east, and an hour later there was a pack howl from the same place. We could not locate any wolves near Shanty Lake.

Again we had a good story—almost too good to be true—but nicely supported by the evidence. A family pack, consisting of two adults and three pups, had become separated, and the parents had laid up at the east end of Shanty Lake for the day. In the evening, after some howling, they started out in opposite directions to look for the pups. Sometime in the night the pups arrived at Shanty Lake, but the parents had gone, so they laid up there for the day. In the evening they heard Basso howling and joined him a mile or more to the east. We will assume that Mello-bell completed her circle and arrived at the same place.

There were many other exciting howling experiences in our Shanty

Yawning.

Lake territory, like the times when our local pack was visited by another from the west and they would howl back and forth across no man's land all night and sometimes all together. The no man's land in this case is a strip running north and south between Shanty and Raja Lakes on which we never find any wolf signs. Whether these boundaries of forbidden land between wolf territories are real or not, nobody is quite sure, but this is not the only example where one certainly seems to exist.

The territory immediately west of Shanty is not regularly used by any wolves, but there are at least three packs in that direction any one of which might come in. As mentioned elsewhere, all parts of a pack's territory do not receive equal use, and this may be a seldom-used part belonging to any one of the three. We know what to expect when they do pay it a visit. After a lot of howling with the Shanty Lake pack, both retreat, one east and one west, but the east pack will be back first, as they commonly spend a lot of time here.

Then there was the time at Half-way House, a stopping place on the way to Shanty Lake, when a pack howled spontaneously nine times in twenty-two hours, and at such unusual times as nine o'clock in the morning and at noon. Something out of the ordinary was going on, but we were unable to find any clues. The world of the wolf is thick with unanswered questions.

Do wolves bark? Some wolves are capable of barking quite as well as a dog, but a barking wolf is heard so infrequently, even in good wolf country, that it seems safer not to assume that all wolves can bark. Adolph Murie is the only one of the better-known sources of wolf information who makes anything of it, and his information is limited to frequent references to wolves that "barked and howled." Barking is not even listed separately in the section on the wolf's voice in *The Wolves of North America*.

The fact that more barking is heard in some packs than in others lends some strength to the idea that it could be an individual characteristic of certain wolves. In the summer of 1964 the park naturalists of Algonquin Park had the Sunday Creek pack and the Madawaska pack under close observation, because they were both close enough to the highway to be used as tourist attractions. In the many times I heard both packs I did not hear a single bark from Sunday Creek, but barking was always conspicuous in the Madawaska pack.

In another chapter of this book Doug Pimlott describes two experiences with barking wolves, and in both cases the wolf seemed to be challenging a close approach to a family group. But an experience of the Huntsville Wolf-listeners is not so easily explained.

This happened at Shanty Lake on October 21, 1962. At that date the pups would be well able to travel, and in fact the pack was apparently off on an expedition somewhere at the time.

Elsewhere I have described the status of the two packs that we commonly found in this area, and on this occasion the situation was unusual in that the west pack was there alone. They howled at 6:00, 6:30, and 10:25 on the evening of October 20, and again at 12:15 on the morning of October 21. Then, at 6:30 P.M. of that day a single wolf began to bark, and occasionally give the lonesome howl, from the same direction as this pack but closer. It was being answered by single howls from a wolf to the east. The barking continued from the same spot for two and one-half hours, and all the time the east wolf was coming closer. At 9:00 the two wolves were together and both howled. There was no more barking, and they moved off to the east, howling occasionally. At 9:30 they were almost out of hearing.

This could still have been a challenge, but we were not the object; the wolf was too far from us for that. Is it possible that it was a member of the Shanty Lake pack that, while hunting on its own, had encountered the strange pack at the borders of its territory, and that it was challenging them? And what of the wolf that came to get it and persuade it to come on home? John Theberge tells of watching two adult wolves when three pups howled a half mile away. The adults replied; then one of them ran off in the direction of the pups and in a short time returned with them.

Although wolves not infrequently howl in the daytime, wolf-howling or wolf-listening are essentially nocturnal activities. And there is a lot more to it than just hearing wolves. There are the nights in fall and spring when wild geese are flying—we hear their calls coming down from the darkness above and we wonder, "Can they hear the wolves, too?"—the spring nights when listening is impossible anywhere near a pond because of the din of frog voices; the whippoorwills; the loons, which are often stimulated to call by the sound of wolf howls; the barred owls, which also commonly answer. At Shanty Lake, one September night, we were listening to wolves howling, a whippoorwill, a great horned owl, and beavers slapping their tails on the lake, all at the same time. It is often foggy on fall nights; travel itself becomes an adventure, and the sound of wolves howling across the shrouded landscape takes on an added mystery.

Both wolf-listening and wolf-howling have their places, but for the average visitor to wolf country, howling is recommended. There is a very real kick to be had out of getting an answer to your own voice from a pack of wolves. Many people are hesitant about trying to howl, but if you are able to make a noise that sounds anything like a dog howling, it will do. Two or three people howling together are better than one, and a mixed "pack" of male and female voices is the best of all.

We cannot hope to promote wolf-howling as an outdoor recreation for everybody. But the howl of a wolf is a direct link with that primeval wilderness from which we all started. The least we can do is to see that we do not deny the possibility of hearing it to those who come later.

Wolves as Individuals

WE LEARNED about wolves as individuals from quite a few wolves, but mostly from a litter of brother and sister wolves, Dagwood, Blondie, Kit, Lupe and Puppet.

During the early days of the Ontario Wolf Research Program we realized that we were not going to have much opportunity to get a very close look at wild wolves. We decided that we should keep a number of captives to observe. There were then two at the Research Station. Both, however, had been captured too late in life to be very happy in their new situation. The remedy, we considered, was to get some very young pups and hand-raise them. That way, we reasoned, we should have adult wolves that would be better adapted to people and under less stress.

The Government of Ontario pays a $15 bounty for wolf pups that are killed, so we made it known that we would pay twice that sum for any that were delivered to us alive. The word that we wanted wolf pups went out through the various offices of the Department of Lands and Forests. In the early spring of 1960, five pups were brought to Moosonee, a town on James Bay, by two Indians who had discovered a den and removed the pups. Soon after they were received in Algonquin Park the Pimlott family moved to summer quarters on Canoe Lake and took over the job of caring for them. During that summer as the pups grew up they had a close association with Peter, Mark, and Janice Pimlott, who were then eleven, ten, and eight years of age. The children fed them, howled with them, walked them beyond the confines of their pen, and gave them names.

Wolves as Individuals

The daily record of their progress soon indicated that we did not have just five wolf pups—we had, in fact, five *individual* wolf pups. Dagwood and Blondie were big blondes, complete extroverts and complete people-lovers. Lupe (after Lupus) was friendly too, but she knew that there were basic differences between wolves and people. She would not be bossed around too much and was always quick to let you know if you overstepped the bounds of propriety. Puppet was the mischief-maker, and the tease of the litter. Nothing was quite safe from his fast-snapping teeth; bootlaces, rubber boots, hats, or a handkerchief that poked from a pocket, were given the permanent imprint of his teeth. If the object was loose it was quickly carried off, and only the hardest chase would cause him to turn belly up and drop it.

From the very first day that the wolves came, it was evident that there was a shy one in the litter. When the other four tumbled out to gobble up a meal, Kit hung back and waited until the person who brought the food, particularly if it was an adult, had retired to a respectable distance. Eventually her reserve broke down with the children. She never quite learned to trust adult humans and always tried to maintain a flight distance that made a close approach difficult to accomplish.

Not long after the pups were settled in the pen that had been built for them behind the Canoe Lake house, they were visited by a neighbor —an old-timer—who had lived in the Park for many years. He "knew everything about wolves" and quickly proceeded to pass on his know-how to the children. "You must be rough with them," he said, as he climbed into the pen and began to give the pups some rough-and-tumble treatment. The pups, who had by then little fear of humans, quickly responded by dashing in and out taking nips, and even some little pieces out of the long rubber waders he was wearing. The children fought valiantly to retain their sobriety as the uninvited guest quickly retreated from the wolf pen, leaving not only bits of rubber but also his dignity behind.

145

A short time later Blondie was taken away to grow up with Siberian huskies that were owned by a member of the Department of Lands and Forests, so our wolf family was down to four.

After returning in early July, 1960, from an extended trip away from the Park, I began to make frequent visits to Potter Lake, about four miles from where we were living. The purpose of my work was to obtain records of two packs of wolves whose ranges appeared to border on opposite sides of the lake. The Potter Lake Pack, as we called the pack on the east side, had a rendezvous site only a mile or so from the lake and could usually be located by its reply to our howls.

My family stated flatly that they had enough house living for the summer and insisted that I just had to work out something so that we could all camp at Potter Lake. The whole idea seemed completely illogical to me, for although we had done a lot of bush living at various times I had never had to figure out what to do with a litter of wolf pups, but my negative approach to the idea did not deter the other members of the family.

One day when I had pulled my canoe up on a little island in the narrows of the lake to have an evening lunch, an idea suddenly occurred to me; "We could camp here; since wolf pups don't like to swim we wouldn't need elaborate facilities to keep them confined."

We moved the pups up to the island on August 7. The first part of the trip by truck went well, but the canoe trip proved to be tricky, for the pups were nervous and could only be taken in the canoe one at a time. Dagwood, who was the last to make the trip, was disturbed at being left behind. He waded out into the water but made no attempt to swim. Soon he too had his turn and joined the other pups, who were exploring the island.

We worked on the island for a time clearing the site for the tents. We checked on the pups periodically to make certain that they were getting settled in their new home. During this time we learned that the way to get wolf pups to come when you want them is to howl for them rather than call them by name. We howled expecting them to reply, but instead they came running to where we were.

Before leaving for the night we fed them heavily, constructed a small watertight lean-to, and put into it the old sleeping bag that they were accustomed to sleeping on.

The next day we returned with our tents and a short piece of wire fence to put around our camp area. We reasoned, and how right we were, that the fence was necessary for self-protection, otherwise everything would be chewed up and/or carried away by the pups. By late afternoon when we had about finished we stopped to have lunch. The pups became aware that food was being served and instantaneously found a dozen ways of getting under, over, through, and around the fence, which we had considered was then wolf-proof. Before we realized what was happening half our lunch was gone. There was a wild melee for a few minutes as we fought for our food and heaved the pups over the fence. It was rather wasted effort, for they promptly found another hole and got back in again. In the midst of it all, as we roared with laughter, I called out, "Shut the doors they are coming through the windows, shut the windows they are coming through the doors." The fence was never completely wolf-proof. However, the pups finally seemed to become aware that the camp yard was not their territory and did not invade very often.

The misconception that wolf pups do not like water was dispelled quickly. Within four days they were swimming around the end of the fence and by the eleventh day from the island to the mainland. Dagwood was the most venturesome. After he got used to the water he would go from full running to swimming without ever breaking his stride.

The realization that the wolves were venturing from the island came as a result of a visit of Dr. Bill Gunn and his wife Ann to Potter Lake. Bill is widely known for his *Sounds of Nature* records and had come to make recordings of the Potter Lake Pack, which was then putting on some very fine concerts from its rendezvous site a half mile east of the lake. After working most of the night, Bill and Ann were awakened early in the morning by two wolf pups putting their heads through the tent flaps. When they got up to check, one pup, presumably Dagwood, licked Bill's hand and wanted to play. They decided then that the pups must be tame. Mark and I had spent the night near the rendezvous site, so when Bill arrived with the news my wife, Dorothy, went looking for the pups. When she found them they were all resting on the north end of the island. Three were still soaking wet; only Kit had remained at home.

Our peace of mind was at an end for the remainder of the summer. Since we still did not know much about tame wolves, we lived in dread that the pups would leave us and take up with one of the wild packs. We even built a small, *really* wolf-proof pen so that we could confine them during our absences from the island.

Late in August, I was invited to give a nature talk at the Amphitheatre in the Lake of Two Rivers Campground. We decided to take Dagwood along to add an air of reality to the occasion. At first he was quite nervous, confined in the back of the panel truck. However, Peter and Mark crawled in with him and he soon settled down.

Dorothy kept him out of sight during the early part of the program, for I was unwilling to meet such tough competition, but near the end, when I was talking about wolf-howling, I brought him on to the platform. At my signal, tape-recorded howls were turned on. Dagwood's ears perked up, and as he hesitated, eight-year old Janice, who had been fidgeting in the shadows beside the platform, jumped up on its edge and began to howl. Instantly, Dagwood put his nose up and joined in with great enthusiasm. It was the first time most of the audience had ever seen a wolf, much less heard a wolf howl, much less heard and seen a child and a wolf howling together, and it brought down the house. More than a thousand people rose in a standing ovation, and the program ended in a rush of congratulations. Six years later, visitors to

Algonquin Park still ask after Dagwood, who, we think, has probably done more toward creating a favorable image of the wolf than any other single wolf in history.

At the end of August, the wolf pups were returned to the wolf pens at the Wildlife Research Station. They were given no more freedom until late in November, when all tourist and camping activity had ended in Algonquin Park.

Early in October, a newspaper reporter came to the Research Station to write a story on the research program and to take some photographs of the captive wolves to illustrate his story. In the course of his preparations he left an extension cord hanging within reach of the pups. Puppet chewed it until only fragments remained. He ingested parts of it and died a few days later.

By December, Dagwood, Kit and Lupe were very close to being adult in size but were still friendly people-loving wolves. During the winter Peter, Mark, and Janice did not visit Algonquin Park and so had no contact with the wolves. I had been working at the Research Station during the latter part of the winter; during the Easter vacation in early April, Dorothy and the children joined me.

The day after they arrived the three children were playing out on the ice of the lake when I released the three wolves from the pen. Soon after the initial flurry of activity around the pen area, visiting other pens and racing back and forth, the wolves saw the children in the distance and raced out to them. It was obviously a very joyous occasion for the wolves, but a rough one for the children. The wolves jumped up on them, stole their hats, and even bowled them over. Mark had the roughest time of all, ending up with a slightly blackened eye and a snow-washed face. By the time I got out to the greeting area, things had quietened down. The wolves, however, were still playing chase with Janice's hat, which was fur-trimmed and particularly likable as far as they were concerned. Finally, with the help of Nutak (our family dog), Peter and I ran them down and recovered the hat.

149

Nutak and Kit.

After the initial greeting was over the relationship of wolves and children quickly returned to the normal pattern of friendly companionship that had been the rule during the previous summer. Although it seemed difficult to credit, during the afternoon following the welcoming-home affair, Dagwood was particularly friendly and gentle with Mark, who had received the brunt of his attention earlier. I was a little concerned that Mark might build up a fear of the wolves, so the next day I encouraged him to enter the pen to visit Dagwood and Lupe. This time there was no roughness to their greeting; both were very gentle and affectionate. Mark's confidence was completely restored.

During the vacation it was Kit who added most to our appreciation of the individuality and personality of wolves. Through the winter she had continued to be wary of me and of others at the Research Station. Often if I had the wolves out for a run I had to resort to trickery of one form or another to get her back into the pen.

Wolves as Individuals

The evening after the welcoming-home affair, I quickly got Dagwood and Lupe into their pen. However, although I worked for over an hour, I was completely unable to commit Kit. Finally I decided to give up. I concluded that since Nutak was around, and she was otherwise alone in the outside world, it was unlikely that she would roam very far.

The next morning I was concerned when there was no sign of Kit. During the morning I frequently thought about her and wondered where

Kit steals a cap.

she could be. Suddenly I remembered three live-capture snares up a trail a half mile or so from the camp. Although I had been checking them every day, they just had not entered my thought the previous evening when I had decided to let Kit remain out of the pen. I immediately put on my snowshoes and rushed up the trail to check. Soon I came to the tracks of a single wolf that had traveled north along the trail. The tracks circumvented the first of the snares, but not the second. The snare had worked exactly as it was supposed to. It had closed down to the stop-lock and formed a perfect collar and tether. The small log to which it was attached had dropped to the ground and then had tangled in the brush when Kit began to pull it away. Although tethered, she was lying quietly and comfortably in the snow.

I had a moment of concern—since she was usually so wary, almost frightened of me, would she panic if I tried to release her? Again, it proved, I was underestimating a wolf. She lay quietly wagging her tail as I approached and showed no fear whatever as I removed the snare. After I released her she ran around me in great playful circles, momentarily forgetting, it seemed, that she did not quite trust me.

Later I tried again to put her back in the pen but with no success. Our relationship had returned to normal, that of mutual respect—from a distance. By this time it had become apparent that Kit was still completely at ease with the three children. Janice, who was then nine, and the smallest of the family, was her favorite. Everywhere she went, Kit was close behind. Usually the relationship was a placid, quiet one, but occasionally the mischievous streak of the wolf came to the surface and a mitt, scarf or hat was stolen, carried away, and often buried.

Finally on Friday, after Kit had had five days of freedom, I decided that she simply had to go back into the pen with the other wolves. As a result of watching Kit's behavior around Janice, a completely new strategy had developed in my mind to get her into the pen without spending hours doing it. All that was required, I decided, was for Janice to walk into an empty pen, with Kit following, and then to close the door behind her. Then I would come along and let Janice out. Kit, I thought, would not come near the door because of her reluctance to come too close to me. I outlined the plan to Janice, who executed it to perfection. Kit was back in her pen in a few minutes, betrayed, I suppose, by her love of Janice.

When I first met Gus, he was eighteen and was living on a Salvation Army farm. He had had a hard childhood and was getting the threads of his life straightened out. I had hired him to help me with some work at my home and had found that he was a hard and willing worker. We needed some help preparing museum specimens at the Wildlife Research Station, so I offered him a job there. That was how he came to meet Kit.

Kit surprised us by taking an immediate liking to Gus. He was fresh-faced, short, and rather lightly built; we thought that perhaps in Kit's eyes he was still a child and so could be trusted.

On May 1 she escaped from the pen when one of the students went

Kit and Gus.

in to do a cleaning job. We tried a couple of times to catch her; however, she was too wary and easily outsmarted us. We did not work very hard at it after that, for we were enjoying having the opportunity of observing and photographing her as she roamed around the Station.

The second day she encountered a porcupine and was fortunate to get off with just two large quills lightly embedded in the skin between her eyes. I remembered her behavior when she had been caught in the snare earlier in the spring, so decided that I would try to remove them. She was lying down in a shady spot by the wolf pen when I approached and knelt down beside her. As I reached for a quill she watched me closely but did not move. Both times as I pulled she closed her eyes and then opened them after the quill had been pulled free.

The following day she disappeared and was not seen again for two days. It seems likely that she was in the company of at least one wild wolf during this absence, for a strange wolf was seen in the camp area at the same time that she first returned.

That weekend the first campers set up their tents in a nearby campground; Kit went down to investigate. As one of the students from the station drove by she was standing warily, ready to take flight, with her head through the flaps of a tent. That ended her freedom; we could not risk having campers complain about marauding wolves.

The next day I commissioned Gus to put her back into her pen. The instructions I gave him were based on the method used by Janice earlier in the spring. It was not quite as easy this time, for Kit was a little suspicious of Gus' motives. However, a few minutes and a few food scraps later and Kit was back in her pen.

Gus' first reaction was one of pride that he had been able to do something that everyone knew that the "Doc" had not been able to do. Suddenly, however, as he watched her through the wire the realization of what he had done came to him. He became very crestfallen and said, "She is going to hate my guts for doing this." I assured him that Kit would not hold a grudge, but he could not be convinced. The next day

154

I opened the door and let him into Kit's pen. Her greeting was warm and friendly; Gus was overjoyed, finally convinced that she still considered him her best friend.

Later in the spring we obtained another litter of wolf pups. This one came from Black Donald, Ontario, an area south of Algonquin Park and close to the southern edge of Timber Wolf range in the province. This time the pups were brought to our home instead of to the Park. We wanted to have close contact with them during their early puppy days, and it was not possible for my family to go to Algonquin Park in early June as they had the previous year.

By this time we had come to have great respect for the vocal ability of wolves, so Dorothy and the children decided to name this litter after famous singers: Pinza, Pons, Caruso, Galli, and Curchi. By the time they were taken to the Park in early July they had been joined by a sixth pup, who was called a very unromantic "Knobby." He had just recovered from rickets, and the name was at least a descriptive one.

A week or so after the two families, the Pimlotts and the wolves, arrived at Canoe Lake in the Park, we made plans to return to the island in Potter Lake with the new pups. We decided that we would also move up Dagwood and Kit so as to have an opportunity to study the behavior of both the pups and the older animals. Although Dagwood and Kit were full-grown wolves by that time, they were still sexually immature, for wolves do not have their first young until they are two years old.

The work of the Crislers that is described in *Arctic Wild* gave us a good indication of what would happen when the pups and the older wolves met. However, reading about something and seeing it are quite different things, and we were anxious to see—to observe for ourselves.

When we took the pups to the island we put them in the pen that was still in place from the previous year. We had decided to give them an opportunity to get acquainted with the older wolves through the wire. We still were getting to know wolves, and we wanted to be certain that the pups would be accepted by Dagwood and Kit before we permitted them to really come together.

When Dagwood and Kit were released from their crates at the edge of the lake, both ran excitedly around, under constant harassment by Nutak, who was always belligerent and made a nuisance of himself if a male and female wolf were both present, although he could get along very well if he was alone with either one or the other. After a few minutes Peter, Mark, and I paddled across to the island, making Nutak swim behind. The two wolves followed along the shore, and when they were at the narrowest part they too swam across. There was much evidence of joy when they saw the pups. They crowded excitedly around the pen, rubbing against the wire. At the same time all the pups except Knobby rushed up to the fence, almost turning somersaults. Knobby paced restlessly back and forth along the opposite fence.

During the day I had a number of jobs to perform, so I left Peter and Mark on the island with the wolves. During my absence, approximately two hours, the older wolves made two forays away from the island. On the first one they went down the road toward Canoe Lake; part way down they met a party of fishermen in a jeep and followed them back. A little later they swam across to the mainland east of the island but soon returned.

As I paddled across, Peter and Mark were sitting on the shore near the pen where the pups were enclosed. As I approached, they walked to the south point, with Dagwood and Kit trotting docilely along at their heels.

The boys said that during my absence there had been two vigorous fights between Dagwood and Nutak. They believed that in one, which occurred near the puppies, Dagwood had been the aggressor and had the better of the fight. If that was the case, it suggested that Dagwood was being influenced by the pups, because Nutak was always the aggressor and had always been dominant in the past.

During my second trip that day, Dagwood and Kit were a terrible nuisance. The boys had to go to the mainland. While they were away, the two wolves pushed under the tent door and got in. They mauled the bread, chewed the butter, and ate other things, including half a ham, that had been left over from dinner. They also "captured" and tried to run away with everything else that was loose in the tent. Fortunately I had built a wolf-proof cache around three trees and about eight feet high, so most of our things—and their food—were well out of reach.

On two occasions later that night we got them all to join us in a howl and were in turn joined by a wild pack far to the north.

The following morning Kit and Dagwood came into the camp area as we were getting our breakfast. They began to get into everything again, to the annoyance of all. Finally, after Dagwood began chewing off the tent ropes, I chased them out. They went but were not much frightened.

It was a rainy, wet morning; when it began to clear about noon we began to wonder about them. They were nowhere to be found. They had left the island. Their tracks on the old road told me they had gone south. I found them three hours later near the Canoe Lake house. I learned later that in the interim they had met a wild wolf and appeared with him in tow at a youth camp on nearby Tepee Lake. Dagwood was a terrible mess; he had found a can of paint, tipped it over, and rolled in it. They walked back to Potter Lake with Nutak and me and quickly swam back to the island when the pups howled.

Early the next morning I opened the door of the pup pen and permitted the pups to join Dagwood and Kit. There followed a period of intense activity and excitement that continued for more than an hour. The "adults" and pups were closely associated throughout the day, and it was obvious that Dagwood and Kit had adopted, and were adopted by, the pups. Both Dagwood and Kit fed the pups several times during the day by the regurgitation method.

Late in the afternoon, Kit swam off the island and headed south again along the road. Dagwood remained with the pups. During the evening Kit came to the Canoe Lake house and spent the night there, close to the pen where there were some coyote and coyote-dog hybrid pups. The next morning she visited several cottages around Canoe Lake. She frightened one woman badly when she jogged along at the woman's heels as she went from a sleep camp to the main cottage.

When Kit returned to the island in midmorning, Dagwood left, again following the old road south. He apparently went directly to the Youth Camp on Tepee Lake. When I found him, he was busy carrying off towels and swim trunks from a dock and burying them in the trees behind a sleep camp. I learned that earlier he had been playing with the children but had been left alone when they had gone to lunch.

The children at the camp were very fond of him and did not want me to take him away. The owner, however, was quite definite; he could not have any recurrences of the visits. I could well understand the way he felt about it, for letters home that started off with "Daddy, I played with a wolf today" would not neccessarily be good advertising for his business.

We realized that the jig was up. Our wolves were too inclined to be people-lovers to permit us to do any more work with them on Potter Island. We crated them up and returned them to their pen at the Wild-life Station. It was a relatively simple matter as far as Dagwood was concerned but it required many hours to capture Kit.

Things went badly for the pups after the "adults" were gone. They became ill with a malady mentioned earlier, listeriosis, that was not diagnosed until they had all died. It was a sad time for all of us, and particularly for Dorothy and the children, who nursed them, as one after another, Knobby, Galli, Pons, Caruso, Curchi, and finally Pinza faded away and died.

After the brief episode at Potter Lake, all the wolves were confined to their pens for the remainder of the year. In early January a welder arrived at the Research Station to make some modifications to the pens

Nutak bowls over Scamp—by this time a large male.

so that the wolves could be moved from one compartment to another with greater ease. All the wolves were much disturbed by the activities of the welder and by the roar of the generator that provided the electricity for his welding tools.

On the third day I was making a trip on snowshoes up the branch of the Madawaska River that extends north of the Research Station. We planned to do considerable work in that area, it was the range of the Fool's Lake Pack, during the winter. My intention was to go at least as far as the Chit Lake Cabin to make certain that it was in shape to be used during the winter.

I decided to take along four wolves, Dagwood, Kit, Lupe, and eight-months-old Scamp, and so get them away from the disturbance for the day. When the doors were opened they poured out and ran at full speed around and around the wolf-pen area with Nutak in full pursuit. It was

159

almost six months since Dagwood and Kit had had the opportunity to really stretch their legs and even longer since Lupe had had her last run. Young Scamp had not known freedom since he was a small pup and did not get into the spirit of the occasion at all. When Nutak and I started to cross the lake, the three older wolves soon followed. Scamp could not seem to break away from the pens. He stood watching us until we had crossed the lake.

It was a cold day. The temperature was 10 degrees below zero and there was a brisk wind that added a high chill factor. This had no influence on the wolves at all; they had their full winter coats and, like their wild brethren, were quite capable of withstanding temperatures of 50 degrees below zero.

The pace that Nutak and I maintained was far too slow for the wolves. The first hour we rarely saw them, for they roamed widely. Most of the time they played and chased at either an easy or a fast gallop, depending on the nature of their interest at the particular moment.

It was late in the morning when we got under way, so after an hour and a half I found a sheltered spot and stopped for lunch. Without giving it a thought I dropped my packsack on the snow and moved off to get some dry wood from an old white pine stump that was nearby. As I was chopping I was suddenly prompted to turn around. It was almost too late, for at that moment Dagwood was withdrawing his head from my packsack. Between his great jaws was the paper bag that held my sandwiches. My anguished roar frightened him and he momentarily dropped the bag. His next grab was not as secure; and as he ran, sandwiches wrapped in wax paper spilled from the bag. Lupe, who was nearby, quickly gathered up a sandwich and raced off. By this time both Nutak and I were in hot pursuit. My shouts and the sudden chase startled them. This, combined with the deep snow, gave us a momentary advantage. Dagwood turned belly up and dropped the bag, which I quickly recovered. Lupe did the same for Nutak, but the dog was no help to me, for he quickly gulped the sandwich that Lupe had surrendered. I returned the remaining sandwiches to the packsack, hung it safely from a high branch and returned to my wood-gathering. Soon there was a brisk fire burning which warmed wolves, dog, and a chuckling man.

During our lunch break the wolves were very restive. Periodically they got to their feet and moved around, often stopping to listen and occasionally howling. I suspected that they were hearing distant wolves, possibly the other animals at the Research Station. I could not, however, hear any sounds, although I listened attentively. Soon after we continued on our way the wolves left and I did not see them again during the afternoon. When I returned to the Research Station, Verne Oke, the Station Manager, told me that they had returned about mid-afternoon, remained for a time around the wolf pens, and then gone away again. I did not give them much thought, for during their first winter they had occasionally been away for three to four hours at a time, and individually for much longer.

By early evening I began to be concerned about them and started making some phone calls. I learned that during the afternoon they had visited a crew that was clearing brush at a nearby campground; later they had visited a tourist lodge a couple of miles away. This established the direction of their travel, so I took a truck and set out to search for them.

A light snow had fallen, and periodically I found the tracks of two and sometimes of three wolves on the edge of the road. As I approached Sunday Creek, eight miles east of the Station, my eyes picked up a dark patch. It was Kit, lying dead, her body partly up on the snow bank. The tire marks and the wolf tracks in the fresh snow told the story. As the car approached she had moved closer to the snow bank to let it pass by. However, on seeing the wolf the driver veered in sharply and hit her. There were no human tracks on the snow. The job finished, the driver kept right on, probably exulting in a job well done.

I was filled with grief, dismay, and self-condemnation—the latter because I realized that I should have been aware that tame wolves were particularly vulnerable to being "attacked" by cars. I continued the search for the other two. Periodically I found tracks and so presumed that Dagwood and Lupe had continued to travel east along the highway. By the time I arrived at the East Gate of the Park, 16 miles from the Research Station, the gateman was off duty, and no one at the staff house had seen or heard anything of the wolves. I went on to Whitney, a village about 4 miles east of the park. The only sign I found was a few tracks on the side of the road about halfway between the East Gate and the village.

On the return trip I stopped every half mile or so, howled, and then waited a few minutes to listen and watch for the wolves. Finally, near the spot where we had seen the last tracks, Dagwood suddenly appeared on the road. I let Nutak out of the truck, and a moment later they were joined by Lupe. I was overjoyed that I had at least two of them unharmed.

I started back to the East Gate, driving very slowly, with Nutak and the two wolves running along behind. It was late and there was little traffic, so our trip was accomplished without incident. From the Staff House I phoned the Research Station for help. John Shannon, another member of the Wolf Research team, said that he would come and bring the two crates we had built to transport wolves. When John arrived an hour later he had two crates but only one door. They had searched for a half hour but had been unable to find the other; finally, they had come without it.

We tried first to catch Lupe, but she was nervous and wary, so we gave up and crated Dagwood instead. We could not find anything to make a door for the second crate, so John decided to take Dagwood back to the Station and make a second trip for Lupe. Nutak and I were to remain behind to make certain that she did not roam away again.

By the time John and his companion left for the Research Station it was 1:30 A.M. It was a calm, clear, cold moonlit night. The temperature was 40 degrees below zero. To keep warm I sat in the truck with the motor and the heater running. Every ten or fifteen minutes I got out and howled to bring Nutak and Lupe back within the range of my vision. At 3 A.M., and about the time I expected the others to return, I stepped out beside the truck to howl. Just as I raised my head I heard the sharp report of a high-powered rifle. Instantly I shouted at the top of my voice, "Don't shoot—it's a tame wolf." A voice replied, "It may be too late." I rushed over to the house of the Ranger who had fired the shot. After a short search we found Lupe's body in a little depression under a pine tree. My first thought was one of condemnation, but by then I felt strongly that the blame was mine and should not, could not in fact, be unloaded on others.

I learned that the Ranger's wife had been awakened by a noise. When she looked out of the window she had seen Lupe silhouetted in the moonlight. Their beagle was sleeping in its house nearby and, fearing for its life, she had awakened her husband. He, who over the years had killed many wolves, had no thought that it might be one of the "Wildlife Wolves." His shot was true; Lupe was instantly killed by the bullet. As I sadly carried her body to the East Gate, the truck returned with the crate that was to have taken her back to the Research Station.

Dagwood became rather widely known not only because of his performance at the Lake of Two Rivers Amphitheatre but also because of three appearances on a national television program. In Canada, hockey is a favorite sport and during the winter occupies considerable prime television and radio time. The uncertainty about how long a game will take means that there must be "filler" shows to round out time slots. The late King Whyte had such a show. It dealt mainly with hunting, fishing, and nature topics. It took up spare time on The Canadian Broadcasting Corporation Network after the National Hockey League game on Saturday night.

Dagwood's first appearance on the King Whyte Show was in 1960, when he was about seven months old. The second and third were approximately a year later and were shared with Scamp.

The trips to Toronto involved a considerable degree of disturbance for the wolves. They had to be crated, trucked 200 miles, held in a crate overnight, and then returned to the Park the following day. It turned out that they had an amazing ability to withstand the stress of these situations and to adjust quickly to the completely strange environment of a large television studio.

On the first occasion we kept Dagwood in the crate until just a few minutes before show time. He was nervous when first released, but after a few minutes of exploration and meeting people, he settled down fairly well.

As a result of this experience we decided that if there were future occasions we would give him, or any wolf, at least an hour to become familiar with the studio and its occupants. We did this on both shows in 1961 and found that it gave the wolves the opportunity that they required to adjust to the strange environment.

During the first half hour Dagwood and Scamp pulled me and John Shannon all over the studio. They investigated cables, cameras, props, and people. They then settled down, usually either resting or quietly getting up to investigate something that was new or that they had not examined before.

The most amusing and interesting incident occurred while we were waiting to go on the air for the second show. The wolves had by then made themselves at home in the studio. Papers for us to sign were brought to the studio by a lovely, and well-perfumed, script girl. Immediately the door opened, Dagwood's nose went up into the air. He quickly located the source of this new olfactory experience. As the script girl approached, Dagwood closed the distance, pulling me along behind. It was obvious from his expression that whatever his intentions were, he at least did not intend to eat her. His face mirrored pure satisfaction as, pulling against his chain, he rose on his hind legs, put his feet on her shoulders and licked her face. There was great hilarity on the part of the onlookers but considerable trepidation on the part of the script girl, who was not experienced enough with this type of wolf to be able to interpret his intentions from his behavior.

The appearances before the television cameras were quite uneventful. On the last two, the wolves lay down quietly, Scamp beside John Shannon, Dagwood by my side, as we talked about wolves and their relationship with men. Scamp did get into the act once when he snarled loudly at King Whyte, who had unintentionally made a sudden move in his direction. King's instinctive response was one of alarm and gave us a laugh, for it illustrated so vividly some of the things we had been discussing.

Some of the foregoing accounts illustrate how my life, and that of members of my family, has been enriched by the opportunity to live close to tame wolves. I have, however, come to feel strongly that it is wrong to take a wolf, or any other large wild carnivore, and treat it as a household pet. Domestic dogs did not acquire their "pet" characteristics overnight. Their domestic ancestry goes back so far into antiquity that it is difficult to come to a conclusion about their origin that is generally acceptable.

The characteristics that make a dog a good household pet have been acquired as a result of the deliberate manipulation of the gene pool by man. The characteristics of the wolf, on the other hand, are the result of the influence of harsh environmental factors. Under natural conditions it is unlikely that many of the characteristics, such as obedience and subservience, that we consider desirable in dogs, would have much survival value to a wolf. Among wild animals, it is the survival value of a characteristic that is likely to dictate whether or not it is passed on to succeeding generations.

Soon after we obtained the first litter of pups in 1960, I began to think about these things. I realized that if we wanted wolves for pets the thing to do would be to keep Dagwood and Blondie, the gentle, placid pair, and dispose of the remainder of the litter. By repeated breeding and cross-breeding of wolves of this type, combined with rigorous culling, one might eventually arrive at a "household" wolf that would be not only tame but also close to being a domestic animal.

However, when people decide to take a wolf, or a lynx, or a lion as a pet they do not do this. They take the first one they get their hands on, though it may very well be the "Kit" of the litter, with few of the characteristics expected of a pet by our society.

My thought about the injustice we do wolves by trying to make ordinary pets of them was reinforced by our experiences with Yukon, who came to us as a result of Dagwood's first appearance on the King Whyte Show. A week or so after the show I received a letter from a trapper who lived near Banff National Park in western Alberta. He had two large adult wolves, one of which he would like to give us. This one, a male, he stated, had been raised by a woman and had been given to him as a young adult. He had intended to use him as a member of his dog team, as he did the other—female—wolf, but it had not worked out. The male just did not work well in a team. Would we like to have him?

We talked it over and decided that we would. We wanted to have animals in the captive population that had had a close association with humans, and this one obviously had such a background. At any rate, there was nothing to lose, for all our trapper friend asked was that we pay the express charges to bring the wolf from Alberta to Ontario.

Yukon, as we named him, turned out to be a magnificent animal. He had come from Yukon and was probably a Mackenzie Valley Wolf, *Canis lupus occidentalis*. At any rate, he was a very big animal and probably weighed between 100 and 120 pounds.

It soon became obvious why the lady had not kept him as a pet and why the trapper had not been able to work him into his dog team. He was very aggressive and appeared to have none of the personality traits that make Dagwood such an appealing wolf to a human. I tried hard

166

to get to understand him but never succeeded. When I went into the pen with him he always watched me very closely and maintained a respectful distance. However, if I turned my back, he would frequently make a quick little rush, breaking off when I turned to face him. On two occasions he nipped the ankles of individuals who were cleaning his cage and had not kept a close watch on him. We soon learned to keep at least one eye on him when we were in his pen.

In his work with wolves at the University of Chicago, Dr. Benson Ginsberg has developed a method of "socializing" wolves. It involves developing the confidence of a fearful or wary animal to the point where it will completely accept and be friendly with humans. The method involves sitting quietly for hours at a time in a small pen with the wolf. The wolf successively goes through stages of fear and aggression before finally becoming "socialized." During the aggressive stage the person involved must display a quiet coolness while the wolf is threatening him, even tearing pieces from the loose clothing that it has been found desirable to wear.

I did not know about Dr. Ginsberg's methods at the time that we had Yukon at the Research Station. He would have made an excellent subject for such research. I feel certain that if Yukon could be "socialized" any wolf could be.

We received Yukon in early January. On the way to the Park from the railway station, a distance of some 45 miles, he chewed his way through the plywood door of his crate and escaped. During the three days it took us to recapture him we learned a little more about the behavior of wolves that have been tamed. For one thing, wolves that have not had experience in a natural environment do not feel at home there. Very quickly they will seek out and associate themselves with people, their pets, and their dwellings and remain very close to them.

This was the only freedom that Yukon had during the winter. Although I was eager to see how he would behave when he got to know an area, I did not feel that I could release him when there was normal activity at the Research Station.

During the same Easter vacation in which Kit was free for several days, I considered the possibility of letting Yukon out of the pen for a few hours. All the conditions were favorable, members of the Pimlott family were the only persons in residence at the Station, and because of the wintry conditions and the holiday period, there were neither campers nor work crews in our part of the Park.

The day after Janice had brought Kit's freedom to an end, I opened the door of Yukon's pen. His response to the outside world was completely different from that of the other wolves, who always raced about excitedly after being released. He was very cautious and moved slowly around the area where the various pens were located. He seemed to be smelling his way about. He stopped frequently to urinate and then to scratch vigorously with both hind and front feet as many male dogs do.

The trapper had told us, when we contacted him for advice on how to recapture Yukon after his earlier escape, that he was particularly fond of women and cheap perfume. We decided to try both on him.

My wife, Dorothy, seated herself in the snow near one of the pens and waited for him to appear. The remainder of the family kept out of the way; the children and Nutak were in the truck, I was back by the wolf pen. When he became aware of Dorothy he approached to within a dozen feet or so of her, whimpering intensely. Dorothy remained in the same position for a considerable period, attempting to coax him to her. However, she was not able to break down the barrier, so eventually she gave up. She had spread some "cheap" perfume around on the snow. After she moved away Yukon spent many minutes vigorously rubbing and rolling on the scented spots.

Later in the afternoon the three children joined me at the wolf pen. At one point we were walking together from the pen to a nearby building that we called the Animal House. Mark was on my left and about a pace behind me, Janice and Peter were on my other side. Out of the corner of my eye I noticed Yukon making a very rapid movement. I turned quickly and found him racing toward Mark, but as soon as I faced him he veered away. One of Mark's mitts was dangling, and I thought that possibly he had been attracted by it as any of the other wolves would have been.

By then the sun was getting low, so Peter and Mark began to prepare to feed the wolves. I decided that Yukon should be returned to his pen. I set the door so it would swing shut when he entered and took the fresh meat that was attached to the "trigger." My plan was to have Yukon follow me past the open door of his pen, see or smell the bait and so be enticed to set off the trap.

When Janice and I saw Yukon coming up the trail toward us, we moved around the pen to pass the door. We had agreed not to look back for fear that we would frighten him away. When we were 30 or 40 feet beyond the door of his pen, Janice, who was behind me, screamed. Yukon had grabbed her clothing just above her rump. At the instant I turned, he released his grip and ran off a short distance. Later examination showed that one of his canine teeth had penetrated her heavy winter clothing, leaving a scratch about 6 inches long on her skin.

We went over to our cabin to give him an opportunity to find his own way back into his pen. When I returned a half hour later the trap had been sprung and Yukon was inside again. A year or so later, when we needed to make room for other wolves that were being added to the

Dorothy Pimlott coaxing Yukon.

captive population, he was donated to the Riverdale Zoo in Toronto. He is still there, living, it seems, quite a contented existence.

Yukon's behavior remains an enigma to me. I do not know how he was treated before he came to us. Perhaps he learned to distrust people when he was a young wolf. At any rate, it was apparent that a wolf with Yukon's attributes would be unlikely ever to make a satisfactory captive or pet. More likely, he would bring disrepute to wolves, convincing all who knew him that the stories about wolves being sneaky, treacherous characters were true.

As a result of our experiences with Yukon and the other wolves, I became convinced that the only way to work with captive wolves is to have them from the time they are very young pups. Then, as they grow up, you gain a deep insight into the personality and behavior of each individual. Confidence in working with animals is based on such understanding and is vital if one is ever to work successfully with wild animals in captivity. I have often wondered if my inability to make friends with Yukon was not as much my fault as his. I found it difficult to be completely confident when there were no barriers between us. It is possible that this may have been the critical flaw in our relationship.

But this too is one of the reasons why wolves should not be considered as conventional pets. Under such circumstances they are constantly required to cope with people who do not understand them and who fear them. This compounds the problem and places them in many difficult situations that wolves should not be expected to face.

Wolves are wild animals. When they are tamed and kept in captivity they should be handled in very special ways. They should have the advantage of facilities that will permit them to have lives of their own, to be wolves and not dogs. I do not mean that they should not have close relationships with people; but such relationships should be restricted to the few who have a real understanding of the animal that is a wolf.

The Future of Wolves

WE DARE TO BE optimistic about the future of wolves in Canada and Alaska. We are, however, pessimistic about their future in Europe and Asia. Finally we are hopeful, but very uncertain, about their chances in the United States and Mexico.

In Europe—and in Russia in particular, where a great proportion of all the wolves in Eurasia exist—the feeling against wolves is as strong as it was in the United States at the height of the war on wolves over fifty years ago. The attitude of Russian scientists I have spoken to and of some others who have written about wolves has generally been unsympathetic. The most common attitude appears to be that wolves are vermin; they kill animals that are desirable to man and so should be exterminated.

In many ways the people of Scandinavia are the most disciplined and thoughtful in the use of the resources of their countries of any in the world. However, when one examines the situation closely it is evident that by far the greatest regard is paid to economic resources. There is a much lower sense of value for competitors such as avian or mammalian predators. It was pointed out in an earlier chapter that there are probably fewer than twenty wolves in all Sweden, a country where hunters kill 30,000 or more moose every year. A population this small, and particularly one where a gregarious species is involved, must be considered in imminent danger of extinction. Kai Curry-Lindahl states in his article, "The Plight of Scandinavia's Large Carnivores," that public opinion seems to be changing; can the change come quickly

171

enough? A single incident, such as a man with a rifle meeting a wolf pack at the right place and right time, could result in wolves being exterminated. It will be to Sweden's eternal shame if it fails to pay the small tithe for the use of the land that keeping wolves requires.

In the United States the only wolves that appear to have any degree of security are those in the Superior National Forest in Minnesota. Since it extends to the Canadian boundary, the possibility of immigration offsets the possibility of the wolf population's suffering a disaster.

The payment of bounty for killing wolves has existed in Minnesota for a long time, so even though the state harbored the last major population of wolves in the country, people were paid $35 to kill them. In 1964 the state legislature passed a bill which would have continued bounties on foxes and wolves. However, the Governor, Karl Rolvaag, vetoed the bill. The Minnesota Conservation Federation and the Minnesota Division of the Izaak Walton League of America, on October 1, 1965, presented him with a commendation plaque for his action. Both organizations had previously gone on record as favoring protection of timber wolves in the state. The respite for the wolves was short, for less than two years later a new governor signed into law a new bounty bill for the state.

The wolves in Isle Royale National Park in Lake Superior are of recent origin, having reached the island in 1948 or 1949. They are completely protected. This does not, however, assure their future, since the environment is gradually changing. It is most likely that the end results of the changes will be a smaller moose herd that can support fewer wolves and possibly even none. Emigration over the ice in winter, disease, or other problems may also at any time eliminate the wolves from the island. The future of the wolves might even be more predictable if the island were not a national park, for then the habitat could be managed to favor the moose, the only source of food for the wolves during the winter.

It seems unlikely that wolves will persist elsewhere in Michigan or

172

in Wisconsin, although it is encouraging that the species now has protected status in both states. In the Upper Peninsula of Michigan the population is estimated at fewer than twenty animals, located principally in the Tahquamenon River Valley. The only hope for the survival of such a small population, in an area that is heavily hunted, is an active protection program. This would have to include a massive public-relations campaign aimed at convincing hunters not to shoot wolves illegally, and intensive research to provide the background knowledge for management programs.

The Michigan Audubon Society has been active in urging total protection of the remaining wolves. Perhaps now that this objective has been achieved it will urge active rather than passive protection as the goal.

In Canada wolves are not in immediate danger, for there are no central organizations, either federal or provincial, whose principal job it is to control noxious animals. Programs now appear to be moderate, and more people are becoming interested in wolves than ever before. The greatest immediate danger is in the Northwest Territories, where the key to the future of the tundra wolves is the Barren Ground caribou. A new book, *Tuktu,* written by Fraser Symington and published by the Canadian Wildlife Service, tells the story again of how the mainland herds of Barren Ground caribou have declined from 2½ million to a tenth of that number. The wolves that live on these herds are believed to number less than 3000. The situation for both species is precarious. If dynamic action is not taken soon to reduce human utilization of the caribou, it will be too late to save many herds.

The wolves face an additional danger—the intensive control that has been undertaken as one of the steps to preserve the caribou. If the control of wolves helps to preserve the caribou, it will, indirectly, be of value to the wolf population too. All the tundra wolves in large areas can at times be concentrated during winter on the ranges of principal herds of caribou. But control programs can go awry. The danger is that under such circumstances control programs will be conducted with only the caribou in mind; that at some time wolf-hating zealots will be in a position where they can disregard official policies which state, "the objective is to control, not to exterminate, wolves." Another danger is that wolf control may become entirely a local matter under the control of the Northwest Territories Council. If this happens, a program aimed at the extermination of the wolves could result.

The principal reason for optimism, for thinking that wolves may someday be generally considered worthy of retaining their niche in the natural environment, is that more and more men are thinking differently about wolves. More and more the positive attributes of these "competitors" are being considered; more and more the veracity of the Red Ridinghood tales in the news media are being questioned.

In our work in Algonquin Park we have found that there is a tremendous interest in this species and that a great many who are showing the interest are relatively uncommitted and so are willing to think about wolves in other than the traditional negative way.

After we learned to locate wolves by the use of tape recordings in 1959 and began to take groups out wolf-howling in Algonquin Park, we soon realized that almost inevitably those who joined us and heard wolves howling were deeply impressed with the experience and anxious to try it again at the first opportunity.

In 1963 the first official wolf howl was held as a part of the interpretive program of the Algonquin Park Museum. We were uncertain about the number that might attend but thought that there might be 25 cars in the cavalcade as we searched for wolves. Instead, every campground emptied; 168 cars—an estimated 800 people—created the biggest traffic jam that had ever been witnessed in the Park. It was not a very successful night in terms of wolves howling; it was however, a howling success in other ways, for the attitudes of those who attended told us better than words that people were thinking positively, not negatively, about wolves.

174

The Future of Wolves

In an earlier chapter, "Spring and Summer," Russ Rutter tells of his experiences with the Sunday Creek Pack in Algonquin Park following the 1964 wolf-listening night. Since 1959, when we first located this pack, their howls have thrilled and excited thousands of people. Many individuals and groups now make special trips to the Park to hear wolves howling. Since the Sunday Creek Pack commonly has rendezvous sites close to the highway, it is the one most commonly heard. In simple ways like this, wolves are gradually attaining a more positive image in the minds of many people. It is a wonderful thing that the wolves themselves are actively participating in this attainment.

The development of an active interest among people is of great importance to the future of wolves in places such as Algonquin Park where wolves have never had protected status. In fact, from the time the Park was established, in 1893, to 1958, killing wolves was considered an important activity of the wardens. The moratorium on the killing of wolves was declared to aid the research program, not to ensure the future of wolves. There is a great deal of public pressure, principally from hunters and trappers, for control of wolves in the Park. It will eventually be undertaken again unless those who appreciate wolves howl in protest.

We have high hopes that throughout the length and breadth of the wolf range the voices of more and more organizations speaking for the wolf will be added to those of The Federation of Ontario Naturalists, to the Michigan Audubon Society, to the Minnesota Conservation Federation, to the Izaak Walton league of America, to the National Audubon Society in the United States, and to the Canadian Audubon Society in Canada.

After we began to study the red wolf in Louisiana, Texas, and Arkansas we heard of Ronald Nowak, who was also interested in them. We became aware of him because everywhere we went he, through his letters, had been before us. He had undertaken his own investigation on the status of the red wolf and wrote to biologists throughout the South seeking information on the red wolf.

Finally he was satisfied that the species really was close to extinction. Then he began to write letters proposing action to save the red wolf. The Louisiana Conservation Department, The United States Fish and Wildlife Service, The United States National Museum, and The World Wildlife Fund were among the organizations that he contacted. One of his proposals for a National Wildlife Refuge for the red wolf has stirred much interest and deserves thorough consideration.

We have high hopes for the future of the wolf because there are more and more men like Ronald Nowak from Louisiana and Dr. Kai Curry-Lindahl in Sweden, who actively espouse the cause and the rights of the wolf.

The future of the wolf is in their hands; it can and it will survive if men learn to understand and hence to appreciate and value it.

Wolves Around the World

THE NAMING of plants and animals—the science of taxonomy—is still a subjective science. In the classification of mammals, a great deal of reliance is placed upon the characteristics of the skull—various aspects of its length, breadth, and height, and some of the teeth.

The genus *Canis* has posed many problems for the taxonomists and indeed for evolutionists. For example, there is probably no taxonomic question that has been argued more hotly than the one pertaining to the origin of domestic dogs. The plasticity of the dogs, domestic and wild, is clearly evidenced by the variation that exists between the Chihuahua and the Huskies or between the Boston bull and the great Dane. This plasticity is in fact the characteristic that causes problems to taxonomists when they try to set up series of measurements, or of other criteria, that will separate the wild dogs, the coyote (*Canis latrans*) from the gray wolf (*Canis lupus*) or either of them from the red wolf (*Canis niger*).

The coyotes of Kansas, for example, seldom weigh more than 25 pounds and so are readily distinguished from the wolves of the arctic tundra, which often weigh more than four times as much and whose skulls are sometimes as big as that of a black bear. However, in some areas there are no marked size differences, and great confusion often results. One of the most interesting areas where such confusion exists between wolves and coyotes occurs in the northeastern states, particularly New Hampshire, Vermont, and New York. Timber wolves were exterminated in the area by the turn of the century, and for many years there were

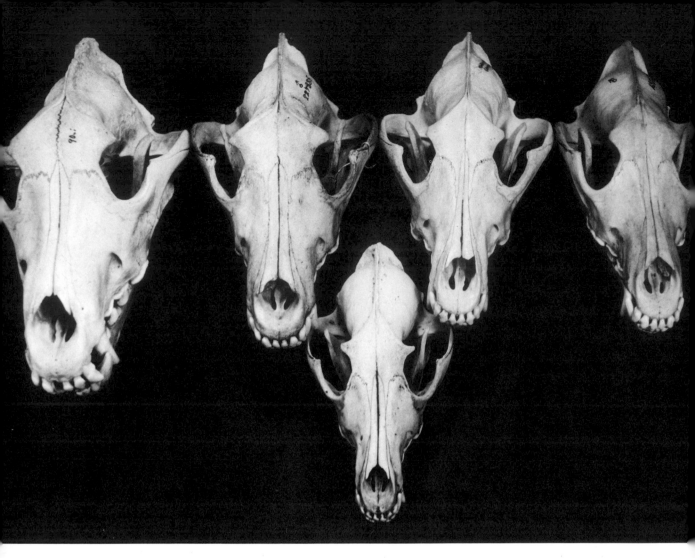

Wolf and coyote skulls. Tundra, Texas gray, timber, and red wolf (left to right); coyote in foreground.

no wild canids. During the past fifteen years, however, reports of a wolf-like animal in the woods have become common, and periodically specimens that have been shot have been sent to state or federal wildlife authorities for identification. The characteristic of many of the animals is that they are of pure wild stock; that is to say, there is no evidence that they are part domestic dog. But from that point on, the picture is by no means clear, since they are frequently so large that they appear intermediate between coyotes and timber wolves.

A litter of the New Hampshire canids was obtained in 1961 and raised by Walter and Helenette Silver of the New Hampshire Fish and Game Department. They are cooperating with Miss Barbara Lawrence, of the Museum of Comparative Zoology at Harvard University, in studies aimed at determining whether the new animals are wolves, coyotes, or hybrids between the two.

In their studies they have been, investigating many of the new methods that are becoming available to animal taxonomists, such as chromatography and protein analysis for identifying the relationships between animals. They are also studying the comparative behavior of their "wolves" and of coyotes from Colorado, as part of their work to answer the question, "What are the new wild dogs of the Northeast?" The fact that it may take years to get the answer illustrates better than anything else that when we think of coyotes, red wolves, or gray wolves we should not be dogmatic in our thinking. The various species and subspecies are still capable of great evolutionary development and change; perhaps that is what has been happening, perhaps the canids of New Hampshire are simply the result of the rapid evolution of wolves or coyotes to take advantage of the greatly changed environment that has resulted from man's use of the land.

With this discussion of the genus *Canis* as background, let us take a look at wolves as they exist around the world.

There is little doubt that the wolf is the most adaptable mammal, other than modern man, that the world has ever known. Before man began to dominate the world, wolves were completely circumpolar in their distribution. In North America they lived from high Arctic areas on Ellesmere Island, Canada, to the Sierra Madre mountains in Mexico and from Vancouver Island in the Pacific to Newfoundland and Greenland in the North Atlantic. The only habitats that they were not capable of adapting to were the deserts and the tropical jungles of southern Mexico. In all probability it was the jungles of Mexico and the rain forests of Central America that prevented them from spreading into and taking over South America as well.

In Eurasia they occupied a similarly wide range. They lived from the British Isles on the west, across Europe and Asia, to the Sea of Okhotsk and the islands of Japan on the east. According to a Russian author, S.I. Ognev, their range extended from the northern limit of reindeer range, at 74 degrees N. in Siberia, south to the Punjab in northern India. In spite of their very wide distribution and common occurrence, the taxonomy of the wolves of Eurasia has not been intensively studied and not nearly as many subspecies have been described as in North America. The following details on the wolves of Europe and Asia are based on a *Catalogue of the Mammals of Western Europe* by G. S. Miller and on *Mammals of Eastern Europe and Northern Asia* by S. I. Ognev.

Wolves of Eurasia:

Canis lupus lupus, The European Wolf.

This was the wolf that originally ranged over much of Europe. It either has been extirpated or is greatly reduced in much of the range where Miller, in 1912, stated that it occurred. During and following the last war it appears to have had a resurgence in parts of eastern Europe. In 1960 the man in charge of wolf control in Poland told me that approximately 1,000 were being killed each year in his country.

Canis lupus deitanus; Canis lupus signatus.

These subspecies were both reported from Spain. The first was very similar to the wolves of other areas of Europe. The second, however, was very different and may have, in fact, been more closely related to the jackal, *Canis aureus,* than to a wolf.

Canis lupus cubanensis; Caucasian Wolf.

The wolves of this subspecies are smaller than those of Central Russia. Their winter pelage is described as being much shorter and thinner, and their summer hair much shorter and redder than the more northern

wolf. Black ones are common particularly in the higher plateau areas.
Canis lupus albus; Tundra or Turukhan Wolf.
This is the large tundra wolf of Eastern Asia. Ognev suggested that it is probably very closely related to the wolves of Northern Alaska, *C. l. tundrarum,* discussed in the review of the North American forms.
Canis lupus dybowski; Kamchatka Wolf.

This subspecies, like many in North America, may not be a valid one, for it was described on the basis of very few specimens. Ognev suggested that it may not be distinguishable from the Turukhan wolf.

Wolves of North America:

The taxonomy of the wolves of North America has been much more thoroughly studied than of the wolves of Europe. In the United States skulls were deposited in the United States National Museum at Washington, D. C., by the trappers of the U. S. Biological Survey, an organization which later became The United States Fish and Wildlife Service. Edward A. Goldman, an American mammalogist, studied this material, as well as wolf specimens available from other sources, and named eleven subspecies. In all, fifteen scientists have their names associated with those of the twenty-four subspecies of the gray wolf, *Canis lupus,* and the three subspecies of the red wolf, *Canis niger.*

In spite of the more intensive North American study, the last word has certainly not been said on the nomenclature of wolves. Some subspecies have been described from woefully small samples. In others, cranial characteristics have been used to separate subspecies that are not at all consistent when a large sample of the animals is studied. In his research at the University of British Columbia, Dr. Pierre Jollicoeur studied a series of more than 500 wolves from the northwestern section of the continent using modern statistical methods. He concluded that far too many subspecific names are probably in use.

The body shape and length of the legs can be quite variable.

Until Dr. Jollicoeur, or some other scientist, makes a thorough review of wolf nomenclature, we have no choice but to stick to the one now in existence. We have, however, placed the two North American species and twenty-seven subspecies into six geographical groups to facilitate our review of them. They are based on reviews of the taxonomy in *The Wolves of North America* by Young and Goldman and in *The Mammals of North America* by Hall and Kelson.

Wolves of the Arctic Islands and Greenland:

Canis lupus arctos, Melville Island Wolf; *Canis lupus bernardi,* Banks Island Wolf; *Canis lupus manningi,* Baffin Island Wolf; *Canis lupus orion,* Greenland Wolf.

The common characteristic of the four subspecies of the high arctic is that, from a distance at least, they are white wolves. On close inspection there may be shades of gray and black hair present; this is not, however, often evident to the observer in the field. A second characteristic is that they are generally smaller than the wolves of the northern mainland which we discuss next.

The prey of the arctic wolves is primarily caribou, and their lives are closely interrelated. Wolves are still present in the four areas from which these subspecies were described.

Wolves of the Continental Tundra and Newfoundland:

Canis lupus tundrarum, Alaska Tundra Wolf; *Canis lupus pambasileus,* Interior Alaska Wolf; *Canis lupus alces,* Kenai Peninsula Wolf; *Canis lupus mackenzii,* Mackenzie Tundra Wolf; *Canis lupus occidentalis,* Mackenzie Valley Wolf; *Canis lupus griseoalbus; Canis lupus hudsonicus,* Hudson Bay Wolf; *Canis lupus labradorius,* Labrador Wolf; *Canis lupus beothicus,* Newfoundland Wolf.

This group of subspecies includes the largest wolves of the world. Stanley Young stated that a large male wolf trapped in east central Alaska weighed 175 pounds and was the largest ever taken by a member of the United States Fish and Wildlife Service. Young considered that the largest wolves in North America lived in Alaska and the Mackenzie River area of Canada. This would probably include the first five subspecies that are named above. Adult males, in these five subspecies, that exceed 100 pounds in weight are fairly common.

The color of the wolves of the continental tundra is much more variable than the color of either the white wolves of the high Arctic or of the gray wolves to the south. For example, a pack of ten animals that was tracked over a 700-mile route in Alaska by Burkholder contained three black and seven gray animals.

It is believed that the Newfoundland wolf was a southern relict of the white wolves of the Arctic. Dr. Austin Cameron considered that Newfoundland was probably colonized by wolves that were carried south on ice floes by the Labrador current. It would seem to be a plausible hypothesis, for both arctic foxes and polar bears regularly show up in coastal areas of Newfoundland and southern Labrador when the ice floes cover the sea.

The disappearance of the Newfoundland wolf poses a very interesting ecological question. There is no historical evidence that they were intensively hunted by man, no drastic habitat changes occurred, caribou were still numerous on the island, yet early in the century they became extinct.

Wolves of the Western Mountains and Coast:

Canis lupus colombianus, British Columbia Wolf; *Canis lupus ligoni,* Alexander Archipelago Wolf; *Canis lupus crassodon,* Vancouver Island Wolf; *Canis lupus fuscus,* Cascade Mountain Wolf; *Canis lupus irremotus,* Northern Rocky Mountain Wolf; *Canis lupus youngi,* Southern Rocky Mountain Wolf; *Canis lupus mogollonensis,* Mogollon Mountain Wolf.

The skull measurements of the wolves of the West suggest that the first subspecies, *C. l. columbianus,* was the largest of this group, probably quite close to the tundra wolves in size. Stanley Young referred to an adult male killed in Washington that weighed 86 pounds, and to another killed in Colorado that weighed 125 pounds. The first was probably a Cascade Mountain Wolf, the second, he stated, was of the southern Rocky Mountain subspecies. It seems likely that wolves weighing more than 100 pounds were probably of rare occurrence among these sub-species.

In color the wolves of this group conform much more to gray and brown shades than to those of the tundra. South of the Canadian border, basically white or basically black animals were rare.

The wolves of this part of the continent have been given a very difficult time by man, and at least the last two subspecies have been exterminated. The British Columbia wolf is still fairly common in the northern part of its range but is rare or absent elsewhere. We are not certain about the status of wolves in the coastal and Archipelago area which was described by Goldman as the range of the Alexander Archi-pelago wolf.

Wolves of Mexico and of Adjacent Areas of the United States:

Canis lupus baileyi, Mexican Wolf; *Canis lupus monstrabilis,* Texas Gray Wolf.

Edward A. Goldman described the Mexican wolf as being the smallest of the American subspecies of *Canis lupus* and comparable in some respects to the timber wolf, *C. l. lycaon.* Dr. Starker Leopold collected an adult male wolf in the Rio Gavilan area of Northern Chihuahua in 1948 that had the lithe-bodied appearance of many timber wolves which we have seen in Ontario.

The Texas wolf was evidently a larger wolf, comparable in size to the buffalo wolf. They differed mainly in color and in characteristics of the skull. The distribution of the two above subspecies was shown by Goldman as extending from southern Arizona, New Mexico and Texas well down into central Mexico. Both have now been exterminated in the United States but may still persist in Mexico. Starker Leopold stated that wolves live in the Sierra Madre Occidental and in the arid mountains of western Coahuila and eastern Chihuahua. He suggested setting aside a park or wilderness preserve as perhaps the only way of saving a remnant of the original population.

Wolves of Eastern and Central North America:

Canis lupus lycaon, Eastern or Timber Wolf; *Canis lupus nubilus,* Great Plains or Buffalo Wolf.

The wolves of these two subspecies originally occurred over almost a quarter of the continental land mass of North America. They were the first of the wolves to come into direct competition with settlers, and as a result they received the brunt of man's efforts at extermination.

The wolves of the Great Plains followed—and lived on—the great herds of buffalo, probably ranging in their migrations from the Prairie Provinces of Canada to the shortgrass prairies of Kansas and northern Texas. The last of the buffalo wolves were exterminated by the early part of the century.

The timber wolves of the East occurred from James and Hudson Bay in Canada south to Florida. They are the predators primarily of woodland caribou, moose, white-tailed deer, and beaver and so do not make the long seasonal movements that were made by the buffalo wolf and are customary to the tundra forms that follow the barren ground caribou. They have been exterminated in the eastern United States but are still common over large areas, including the greater part of Ontario and Quebec.

The buffalo wolf was comparable to the wolves of the tundra with respect to variability of color. Goldman stated that many variations occurred. The timber wolf, however, is much less variable and the percentage of normal-phase animals is large. "Normal-phase" refers to wolves that are grizzled gray on the back, sides and tail, with white bellies and throats, and whose ears are a rich chestnut color on their

White wolves are often shaded with black.

rear faces. Virtually all these animals, and many in other color phases, have a distinct black spot about six inches down from the bases of their tails. The uniformity of the color of timber wolves in many areas is evidenced by the work in Algonquin Park, in Ontario. There, over the past eight years, dozens of packs have been observed from the air. However, we have never been able to discriminate between any of them on the basis of the color variation of individual animals.

The timber wolf rarely reaches 100 pounds in weight. Over an eight-year period the carcasses of several hundred wolves were weighed in the laboratory of the Department of Lands and Forests at Maple, Ontario. The biggest one weighed 117 pounds. It was killed near Hudson Bay and was probably a tundra wolf, *C. l. hudsonicus*, rather than a timber wolf. The others were most commonly in the 60- to 80-pound range. Each year an occasional one approached 100 pounds in weight and probably did weigh that much when it was killed.

The Red Wolf *(Canis niger)*:

Canis niger niger, Florida Red Wolf; *Canis niger gregoryi,* Mississippi Valley Red Wolf; *Canis niger rufus,* Texas Red Wolf.

The problems that sometimes arise in attempting to answer the question, "What is a species?" are very well illustrated by the problems that arise when one tries to separate a series of skulls that includes red wolves, coyotes and gray wolves.

In his description of the red wolf, Goldman stated that it approached the coyote in form but was usually larger. In comparing it with the gray wolf he stated that it was usually much smaller but that some individuals might be larger than small gray wolves. He wrote that the most reliable characteristic in distinguishing gray wolves from red wolves was a little knob, called cingulum, on the upper carnassials, or shearing teeth of the red wolf. However, here too, there are many inconsistencies, for occasionally a timber wolf, even in Canada, has a pronounced cingulum, and occasionally a red wolf does not have one. On the other side of the problem, that of separating large coyotes from small red wolves, the cingulum is of no help at all, for coyotes almost always have them too.

An interesting part of the problem is that red wolves become progressively smaller from east to west across their range. In eastern Texas and Oklahoma, where the range of the small Texas red wolf intergrades with the range of the coyote, there are dozens of these animals that have been killed that are difficult to classify.

It is virtually impossible to separate coyotes and wolves on the basis of color or other pelt characteristics. In the eastern and southern states the majority fall into the normal color phase that we described for the timber wolf. For a long time it was believed that the presence of black wolves was definite proof that an animal was a red wolf. This no longer appears to be the case, for in a recent study we obtained the carcasses of a number of black animals which were not nearly big enough to be considered red wolves. Dr. Howard McCarley, of Austin College in Sherman, Texas, recently made a study of a considerable number of red wolves and coyotes. His study included recent and old collections from a number of museums and collections which he had made in eastern Texas. He concluded that the Texas red wolf was probably a hybrid between the red wolf and the coyote and not a pure red wolf at all.

But what about the red wolf and the gray wolf? Should they be considered to be completely separate species? Is it logical to consider that slight variations in size, color, and the form of teeth and skulls indicate that the wolves of the South Central States are a separate species? The answer is not at all clear, for there are threads of evidence that point first one way, then another. It will have to be left with the taxonomists, who now, after years of measuring skulls and comparing sizes and color shades of pelts, are looking into new and more imaginative ways of answering the question, is the red wolf a good species? Whether or not the red wolf qualifies as a species is perhaps more of an academic question than anything else; it is the wolf of the South Central United

States, whatever the specific name men decide is the correct one for it. The important question, and one which is not academic but a very present reality, is, "Will it be exterminated?"

Until quite recently the red wolf was generally believed to be doing quite well in at least part of its original range in the southern states. In June, 1964, for example, a statement from the Chief of the Bureau of Sport Fisheries and Wildlife of the United States Fish and Wildlife Service was presented to the Committee on the Preservation of Land Mammals of the American Society of Mammalogists. It stated that the red wolf was common in Louisiana, Arkansas, and in eastern portions of Texas and Oklahoma. There were, however, both scientists and laymen who believed that this was not true.

Dr. McCarley's study led him to conclude that a great majority of the animals that were being called red wolves were really coyotes. In the recent collections that he studied, the only specimens that were red wolves were in the Museum of Natural History at Louisiana State University. They had been killed in the bottom-land forests along the Mississippi River and in a section of the coastal marsh country. Dr. McCarley stated his conviction about the status of the species in clear terms, "At present (1961), *Canis niger* is extant only in a few places in eastern and southern Louisiana."

Stimulated by Dr. McCarley's report, a group from the University of Toronto, Canada, studying the ecology of wolves, applied to the United States section of the World Wildlife Fund for a grant to conduct a study of the status and ecology of the red wolves. The request was granted and I left for the South to study the red wolf. I was accompanied by a graduate student, Paul Joslin, who, it was planned, would conduct the study as his doctoral research program. Our field studies conducted during 1964 and 1965 confirmed Dr. McCarley's conclusions that red wolves are very rare.

Simultaneously with the field investigations, but as a completely separate effort, Dr. John L. Paradiso of the U. S. National Museum began to study the status of the red wolf. He obtained large series of these animals from trappers of the Predator and Rodent Control Branch (PARC), of the U. S. Fish and Wildlife Service, who operate in some of the southern states. By August, 1964, he had completed a preliminary study of the skulls. He concluded that not a single specimen in the collection could be identified unequivocally as a red wolf.

In the face of the evidence from the three studies, the official status of the red wolf was reconsidered, and in March, 1965, less than a year after it had been reported as being "common",—it was placed on the list of rare and endangered species of the United States.

In the course of the field study an additional ray of hope began to glow. A number of trappers from PARC stated that there were some areas where especially large wolves were periodically killed. In the spring of 1965 specimens from such an area, Chambers County in southeastern Texas, were submitted to Dr. Paradiso at the National Museum. He identified them as red wolves. Soon after, Paul Joslin began to work in the area. He found additional evidence that some red wolves are present on some of the large ranches in the area.

The Ozark National Forest of northwestern Arkansas may also have a small population. Possibly there are other isolated areas where the red wolf still exists and, once they are located, action may be taken to preserve them. At least we are now aware of the danger—aware that if we do not learn quickly about its way of life, and take rapid means to preserve it, one of North America's most interesting animals will be gone. All that will be left will be a few skulls and skins in museums as the ironic echoes of a hollow question, "Is it a good species?" reverberate down the corridors of time.

Bibliography

Allen, Durward L. and L. David Mech. "Wolves Versus Moose on Isle Royale." *National Geographic,* 123(2):200–219 (February, 1963).

Banfield, A. W. F. *Populations and Movements of the Saskatchewan Timber Wolf in Prince Albert National Park, 1947 to 1951.* Wildlife Management Bulletin, Series 1, No. 4, Canadian Wildlife Service, Ottawa, 1951.

————. "The Range of Individual Timber Wolves." *Journal of Mammalogy,* 34(3):389–390 (1953).

————. *Preliminary Investigations of the Barren-Ground Caribou,* Part II, Wildlife Management Bulletin, Series 1, No. 10B. Canadian Wildlife Service, Ottawa, 1954.

Bates, M. U. "Always Cry Wolf." *Hunting and Fishing in Canada,* 35(9):18–23 (September, 1964).

Bodsworth, Fred. "An Even Break for the Peaceful Wolf." *Maclean's Magazine,* 24, 25, 43, 44 (January 17, 1959.)

Burkholder, Bob L. "Movements and Behavior of a Wolf Pack in Alaska." *Journal of Wildlife Management,* 23(1):1–11 (1959).

Burroughs, R. D. "Last Stand of the Michigan Wolf." *Michigan Conservation,* XXIII(1):33 (1954).

Cameron, Austin W. *Mammals of the Islands in the Gulf of St. Lawrence.* National Museum of Canada, Bulletin No. 154, 1958.

Catesby, Mark. *The Natural History of Carolina, Florida, and the Bahama Islands.* 2 vols. London. 1743 or 1771.

Bibliography

Clarke, C. H. D. "The Beast of Gévaudan." Unpublished manuscript. Fish and Wildlife Library, Department of Lands and Forests, Maple, Ontario. Undated.

Cowan, Ian McTaggart. "The Timber Wolf in the Rocky Mountain National Parks of Canada." *Canadian Journal of Research*, Section D, 25(5):139–174 (1947).

Crisler, Lois. *Arctic Wild*. Harper and Brothers, New York, 1958.

Curran, James W. *Wolves Don't Bite*. The Sault Daily Star, Sault Ste. Marie, Ontario, Canada (1940).

Curry-Lindahl, Kai. "The Plight of Scandinavia's Large Carnivores." *Animals,* 7(4):92–97 (1965).

de Vos, Antoon. "Timber Wolves Killed by Cars on Ontario Highways." *Journal of Mammalogy*, 30(2):197 (1949).

Dunne, Aubrey L. "Report on Wolves Followed During February and March, 1939." *Canadian Field-Naturalist,* LIII(8):117 (1939).

Errington, Paul. "Predation and Vertebrate Populations." *Quarterly Review of Biology,* 21(2):144–177 and 21(3):221–245 (1946).

Freeman, R. S., A. Adorjan, and Douglas H. Pimlott. "Cestodes of Wolves, Coyotes, and Coyote-Dog Hybrids in Ontario." *Canadian Journal of Zoology,* 39:527–532 (1961).

Goldman, Edward A. "Classification of Wolves." *The Wolves of North America.* The American Wildlife Institute, Washington, D. C., 1944.

Hall, E. Raymond and K. R. Kelson. *The Mammals of North America.* The Ronald Press, New York, 1959.

Handbook of Travel. Harvard University Press, Cambridge, Mass. 1935.

Harding, A. W. "The Wolf in Scotland." *The Scots Magazine,* December, 1960.

Ingstad, H. *Nunamiut.* George Allen and Unwin, London, 1954.

Jollicoeur, Pierre. "Multivariate Geographical Variation in the Wolf." *Evolution,* XIII(3):283–299 (1959)

Joslin, Paul W. B. "Summer Activities of Two Timber Wolf Packs in Algonquin Park." M.A. Thesis, Department of Zoology, University of Toronto, 1966.

Kolenosky, George, J. Shannon and R. Standfield. *Some Facts About Predator Research and Management in Ontario.* Mimeograph, Wildlife Section, Research Branch, Ontario Department of Lands and Forests, 1964.

Leopold, Aldo. *Game Management.* Charles Scribner's Sons, New York, 1933.

Leopold, A. Starker. *Wildlife of Mexico.* University of California Press, Berkeley, Calif., 1959.

McCarley, Howard: "The Taxonomic Status of Wild Canis in the South Central United States." *The Southwestern Naturalist,* 7(3–4):227–235 (1962).

Makridin, V. P. "The Wolf in the Yamal North." *Zoologicheckii Zhurnal,* XLI(9):1413–1417 (1962). Translated by Peter Lent.

Matheson, Colin. "The Grey Wolf." *Journal of the Society for the Preservation of the Fauna of the Empire.* Part L. 31–42 (December, 1944).

Maynard, Leonard A. and John K. Loosli. *Animal Nutrition.* McGraw-Hill, New York, 1956.

Mech, L. David. *The Wolves of Isle Royale.* National Park Service, Department of the Interior, Fauna Series No. 7, 1966.

Miller, Gerrit S. *Catalogue of the Mammals of Western Europe in the Collection of the British Museum.* British Museum, London, 1912.

Murie, Adolph. *The Wolves of Mount McKinley.* National Park Service, Department of the Interior, Fauna Series No. 5, 1944.

Murie, Olaus J. *A Field Guide to Animal Tracks.* Houghton Mifflin Company, Boston, 1954.

Nagel, W. O. "Predators Are Like People." *Missouri Conservationist,* 17(1):1–3 (January, 1956).

Novikov, G. A. *Carnivorous Mammals of the Fauna of the U.S.S.R.* Zoological Institute of the Academy of Sciences of the U.S.S.R., Moscow, 1956. Published for the National Science Foundation, Washington, D.C., and the Department of the Interior, U.S.A., by the Israel Program for Scientific Translations, Jerusalem, 1962.

Bibliography

Ognev, S. I. *Mammals of Eastern Europe and Northern Asia.* Volume II, 1931. Published for the National Science Foundation, Washington, D.C., and the Smithsonian Institute by the Israel Program for Scientific Translations, Jerusalem, 1962.

Parmelee, David F. "Myth of the Wolf." *The Beaver,* Outfit 295:4–9, (Spring, 1964).

Peterson, Randolph L. "A Record of a Timber Wolf Attacking a Man." *Journal of Mammalogy,* 28(3):294–295 (1947).

Pimlott, Douglas H. "Wolf Control in Canada." *Canadian Audubon Magazine,* 23(5):145–152 (November–December, 1961).

———. "The Use of Tape-Recorded Wolf Howls to Locate Timber Wolves." Unpublished paper presented at the 22nd Midwest Wildlife Conference, Toronto, 1960.

———. "Wolf Predation and Ungulate Populations." In press. *American Zoologist.*

Plotnikov, D. "The Dangerous Predator Will Be Exterminated." *Hunting and Hunting Economy.* Pp. 21–22. September, 1964. Translated from the Russian by A. Adorjan.

Rutter, Russell J. "Voice of the Wolf." *Nature Magazine,* 51(5):258–260 (May, 1958).

Sampson, F. W. "Missouri's Vanishing Wolves." *Missouri Conservationist,* 22(6):5–7 (June, 1961).

Schenkel, R. "Behaviour Studies on Wolves." *Behaviour,* 1(2):81–129 (1947). Translated from the German by Agnes Klassen.

Schönberner, Dagmar. "Observations on the Reproductive Biology of the Wolf." *Zeitdchrift für Säuzetierkunde,* 30(3):171–178 (1965). Translated from the German by S. Van Zyll de Jong.

Scott, J. P. "The Social Behavior of Dogs and Wolves." *Annals of the New York Academy of Sciences,* 51(Art. 6):1009–1021 (1950).

Stenlund, Milton H. *A Field Study of the Timber Wolf on the Superior National Forest, Minnesota.* Minnesota Department of Conservation, Technical Bulletin No. 4, 1955.

Symington, Fraser, *Tuktu—The Caribou of the Northern Mainland.* Canadian Wildlife Service, Department of Northern Affairs and National Resources, Ottawa, 1965.

Theberge, John B. "Some Aspects of Timber Wolf Howling." Ontario Agricultural College, Fourth Year Wildlife Biology Thesis, 1964.
————. *Howling as a Means of Communication in Timber Wolves.* M.A. Thesis, Department of Zoology, University of Toronto, 1966.
Thompson, Daniel Q. "Travel, Range, and Food Habits of Timber Wolves in Wisconsin." *The Journal of Mammalogy,* 33(4):429–442 (1952).
Tinbergen, Niko. "Polar Teamwork." *Animals.* 1(19):506–511 (1963) (Canadian Edition).
Turi, J. *Turi's Book of Lappland.* Jonathan Cape, London, 1931.
Young, Stanley P. *The Wolf in North American History.* Caxton Printers, Caldwell, Idaho, 1946.
———— and Edward A. Goldman. *The Wolves of North America.* The American Wildlife Institute, Washington, D.C., 1944.

Index

197

Index